ROY M. HUMBLE

WHILE YOU SLEEP
A PERSONAL JOURNEY IN ANAESTHESIA

Published by

MELROSE BOOKS

An Imprint of Melrose Press Limited
St Thomas Place, Ely
Cambridgeshire
CB7 4GG, UK
www.melrosebooks.com

FIRST EDITION

Copyright © Roy M. Humble 2011

The Author asserts his moral right to
be identified as the author of this work

Cover designed by Jeremy Kay

ISBN 978 1 907040 78 8

Printed and bound in Great Britain by:
CPI Antony Rowe. Chippenham, Wiltshire

FSC
www.fsc.org
MIX
Paper from
responsible sources
FSC® C013604

For Betty, who did all the real work,
and for Ken Slack, Andrew Doughty and the late Norman Eve,
who introduced me to the science of anaesthesia.

CONTENTS

Acknowledgements   vii

A fairly responsible job   ix

PART ONE – TRAVELLING FORWARD   1

Gods and Teachers

The day God came to call   3

Three teachers   10

The wrong choice?   14

Students and Doctors

Just another evening on call   16

A Dublin tradition   20

Four men in a car   25

The Doctor   32

Sand and Service

Cairo and the Pyramids   41

An irreverent view of the Army   44

City in the sand   48

Escape from Suez   51

Travel and Training

The White Highlands   55

Masters of their craft   61

In at the deep end   67

From Rhodes to Livingstone   73

Diagnosis and Prognosis

A question of lifestyle   80
Many different faces   83
The VIP   86
A difficult decision   88

Living and Learning

The road to Mombasa   91
A hallowed hall   98
From Boston to Dumfries   105
Contrast and change   112

Photographs   **121**

PART TWO – LOOKING BACK 129

Connections

The flying death   131
A great dream   138
Harvest delayed   147
A man from the East   150
The final pieces   155

Lessons

Ancient and modern   158
Something of value   165
All in the day's work   174

Envoi   179

ACKNOWLEDGEMENTS

I wish to acknowledge the following for their kind permission to include images of classic artefacts under their care: the Association of Anaesthetists of Great Britain and Ireland for the replica of John Snow's ether inhaler, Wellcome Library, London for Joseph Clover's demonstration of his method of using chloroform, the Arthur E. Guedel Memorial Anesthesia Center in San Francisco for the photograph of Richard Gill observing the preparation of curare in Ecuador in 1938 and the Hunterian Museum at the Royal College of Surgeons for the scene painted by an unknown artist which can still remind us of the suffering endured by past generations. The now almost quaint picture of how patients were once anaesthetised by the Vernon Harcourt inhaler comes from D. W. Buxton's early textbook, *Anaesthetics and their uses and administration*, 6th edition, published by H. K. Lewis in 1920.

This book has been a number of years in the making. Its progression from the early draft stages could never have happened without the enthusiasm of web expert Howard Page and the encouragement and editorial advice of my daughter, Noreen Humble. Many other friends have been very supportive, including Brendan Finucane, John Lilley, Roger Maltby and my university classmates Ronald Howie and Iain Glen. My sincere thanks are also due to photographer Angus McDougal of Dumfries, to my cousin Ian Humble for his work in restoring the old photograph of his grandfather, to Dato' Seri M. Mahadevan for his story "A man from the East", to Jean, Lady Polwarth for allowing me to share the studio portrait of her great uncle, R. B. Cunninghame Graham, and finally to everyone at Melrose Books for bringing the completed project to life.

Calgary, Alberta
August 2010

A FAIRLY RESPONSIBLE JOB

My first introduction to anaesthesia came when I lost my tonsils at the age of three. When I was old enough to be told such things I was surprised to find out that the operation had not been done for any medical reason. Since my older brother's tonsils had been removed, mine had to follow before they had a chance to cause a problem. My mother used to regale guests with the story of how I had then demanded food – and demolished it – on returning home a few hours after the surgery at the old Dumbarton Cottage Hospital. She plainly considered me a stoic. The more likely explanation was a strong objection to being starved! Although I had one of Glasgow's best anaesthetists for my next operation four years later my memories are less than happy, the sudden sweetish smell and later wretched awakening suggestive of his use of both chloroform and ether. When another miserable return to consciousness followed the removal of my acutely inflamed appendix in 1946, something of a negative image may have been left in my mind. An inauspicious encounter with an anaesthetist as a third year medical student did nothing to change that perception and by the time we received our degrees anaesthesia was quite unthinkable as a career choice.

Setting down the story now of how this early mindset came to change and how a once scorned speciality took me half around the world, my thoughts go back first to the late 1960s and an afternoon of golf. I was playing a match at the Dumfries and County course in the south-west of Scotland, playing rather better than usual, in fact, as I was already two up on my opponent and had just followed a long and straight drive at the par five seventh hole with an equally successful three wood. As we continued on down the fairway my opponent asked me what I did for a living. I told him that I worked as an anaesthetist at the local Infirmary. 'That's a fairly responsible job,' he replied. We chatted about the subject over the next few holes and my lead began to evaporate. Had he read Stephen Potter's books on gamesmanship, I wondered later, distracting me from the matter in hand, or was he simply being friendly? Either way I never quite got back to my best game and finished up losing the match before the eighteenth hole.

Although I only knew that golfing adversary for a few hours, the significance of his casual remark stayed with me. If the responsibility inherent in our job is obvious to some, why do we remain anonymous figures compared to our surgical colleagues? One typical portrayal of our setting outlines "a surgical team headed by a skilled surgeon which includes other doctors plus nurses and medical technicians". Lost in the words "other doctors" are the anaesthetists (or anesthesiologists). Are they less skilled, as the sentence appears to imply, and their role therefore of lesser importance? They give anaesthetics, but what exactly does that mean? They put people to sleep, but what happens after that and what are their other responsibilities?

Newer ways of answering such questions have emerged. World Anaesthesia Day is commemorated in some countries, a National Anaesthesia Day marked in others. The internet allows public access to information as never before and in Britain even the politicians have taken some interest, an exhibit on anaesthesia a number of years ago breaking new ground in the House of Commons. On the other side of the Atlantic a search for greater recognition as physician specialists has led Canadian anaesthetists to change the name of their Society and adopt the term *anesthesiologist* in the manner of their American colleagues. They have also replaced their original Greek motto (in English *we watch closely those who sleep*) with a modern counterpart – *Science, Vigilance and Compassion*. Unless these kinds of advances can include a much greater personal element, however, they may meet with only limited success. A recent headline "Actually, we are doctors", however tongue-in-cheek its use in a short article for an exclusive readership of anaesthetists, underlines this fact.

Although change may be the order of the day in the new millennium, the significance of that old motto remains the same. I always considered it part of our responsibility to shelter patients from the fact that such sleep can sometimes be far from uneventful, even in seemingly healthy individuals. Now I am not so sure. In this era of increasing consumer knowledge it may be time to take a different and entirely individual approach, one that will make members of the general public fully aware of the trials and tribulations of everyday anaesthesia, the action behind the mask which they cannot see.

So let me share my journey with you, taking you from early heroes and carefree student days to army service in North Africa, from the sand of Suez to a plague of locusts and from the ruins of the old Roman city of Leptis Magna to the Great Rift Valley and the Victoria Falls; from partnering a golfing legend to a wonderful story of hypnosis by the roadside; from hazards in ill-equipped and isolated settings to routine days and stressful nights in major modern hospitals as we moved from the last hurrah of chloroform and ether to the highly sophisticated technology of today; and finally through some of the pages of medical history and the stories of the pioneers who led the way. Many shared the different roads I took. This book is the only way I have of saying thanks.

PART ONE
<u>TRAVELLING FORWARD</u>

GODS AND TEACHERS
THE DAY GOD CAME TO CALL

Like to a god he seems to me…
Catullus (87-54? BC)

What factors determine one's early memories of life? Age is probably less important than might be imagined, the setting and behaviour of other individuals of much greater significance. Although I was only five, I can remember the death of King George V. Well, not actually that death itself, but certainly the funereal music coming from the radio, the hushed conversation in our house and the silence urged upon me by my parents. Many years later I heard a recording of the BBC's coverage of the event. The historic broadcast included a repeated sonorous announcement that the life of the King and Emperor was passing peacefully to a close, seemingly confirming the grandeur of my childhood memory. In that pre-television era, however, the realities of life could easily be sheltered from the public. It is now common knowledge that this particular royal death was far from tranquil, deliberately hastened at the end by the attending physician and with its timing then withheld from the public for several hours in order to obtain the maximum effect in the press. Earlier still, two months after my fourth birthday, I vaguely recall my first day of school at the old Dumbarton Academy, and I can summon up hazy images of being a bystander that September in a stone-throwing confrontation with boys from the opposite religious persuasion to our own. Intolerance was a fact of life in the West of Scotland during the 1930s.

I mention these somewhat blurred pictures to set them against my earliest distinct memory. Although I could be mistaken in the year, it must have been 1933 or the first half of 1934. Memorable would hardly be an adequate description, for I don't imagine many have the privilege of recalling a visit from God. To my young mind this visiting Personage had to be a Supernatural Being. Why else the fuss and flurry that surrounded me, why these seemingly endless preparations? All her life my mother hated the thought that any guest might somehow notice an overlooked speck

3

of dust, or, heaven forbid, a cobweb on a high ceiling. Such efforts were redoubled on this particular occasion, accompanied by firm instructions that small people were expected to be seen but not heard, a standard injunction in those far-off days.

Some memories are sketchy, others crystal clear. With my nose hard pressed against the front window, God's arrival in a seldom seen chauffeured car was notable enough, the impact reinforced by a regal walk up the short driveway of our house on Oxhill Road. The subsequent brief moment is completely frozen in time. I tried to make myself as invisible as possible, as instructed, pressing my back hard against the wall of our narrow hallway. The visage of our guest did not disappoint. Tall and erect, with a full head of white hair and a fine beard, homburg and cane in hand. God must look like that, surely, especially when He presents – with some ceremony – a strange rope-like object[1] to one's elder brother? A blessing in the form of a pat on the head, and then the image fades.

God? About as close as one could get! Our visitor, often referred to at that time as the uncrowned King of Scotland, was none other than the humanitarian Robert Bontine Cunninghame Graham, affectionately known as Don Roberto, descended in direct lineage from Robert II of Scotland and with a stronger claim to his native throne than any member of the House of Windsor. God could have had no less of a welcome, for the worship of my mother came in similar terms. She treasured every brief, scrawled communication from the great man and loved to recall the occasion when she and my father were his guests at a fashionable London restaurant, relishing the regal reception which the staff afforded their host even more than the splendid meal. Cunninghame Graham's estate at Ardoch was only a couple of miles from our home and my father served as his family doctor during the periods he lived there.

When he died in Argentina in 1936 at the age of eighty-three during a last nostalgic return to his spiritual second home, the authorities in Buenos Aires honoured him with a state funeral, his body later returning to Scotland by sea. The elaborate mahogany coffin, a gift from the Argentine government, was removed from the hearse at Ardoch for a short service, resuming its long journey then towards the ruined island priory on the Lake of Menteith. Aimé Tschiffely, Don Roberto's friend and chosen biographer, included this story among his final memories:

> One of those present, an elderly, round-faced old man who was
> dressed in an exceedingly long and roomy frock-coat and who
> wore a peculiar black velvet scull-cap, brought a note of humour
> to the sad proceedings. A few moments before the service was
> about to begin, this wily Scot came to the corner where Captain

---

1.   A lasso, the noosed rope used by the South American gauchos.

Cunninghame Graham,[2] a lawyer and I were conversing in hushed tones, and said with a broad Scottish accent, pointing to the coffin: 'Whit guarantee hae we that Meester Graham's body is in there?' Obviously the good man wanted to be quite sure that Scotland had not been deprived of a treasured possession.[3]

My parents attended the observances at Ardoch and the subsequent church service at Port of Menteith, later standing bare-headed among the gathering on the shore as small boats ferried the main funeral party across the Lake for the final prayers and burial on Inchmahome. Tschiffely's colourful idolatry is evident in the closing lines of his biography:

And so we left our friend, resting alongside his wife and among some of his ancestors... Perhaps, someday, during a warm summer night, whilst the chanting of the Augustinian monks will be heard in the priory, Mary Queen of Scots (again a child), will laugh and chatter with her playmates in the garden and bower of boxwood, where she spent her only happy days. King Robert the Bruce and the Earls of Menteith and other spirits of the Past will assemble in the banqueting hall of the now ruined castle of the Grahams on the island of Inchtalla. When the mists will rise from the lake, to shift over the heather-covered hills, assuming the appearance of Arabian dancer's veils, and the lapping of waves and the murmur of wind in the trees and bulrushes will gradually change into the soft twanging of guitars, the whinnying of a horse will be heard, and Don Roberto, seated on his fiery mustang, Pampa, will ride on...

To the casual onlooker Argentina and Scotland appear to have little in common, yet Cunninghame Graham became a hero of both cultures. What manner of man was this remarkable Scot? His eyes have followed me all my life, looking down from a fine studio portrait taken, I think, in the late 1920s. They continue to do so now as I type these words, just the hint of a challenge in them, daring me to suggest an answer to my own question.

'What manner of man was he not?' seems the most appropriate response. With facial features inherited from a Catalan grandmother, his often flamboyant image graces the walls of art and portrait galleries around the world, from Glasgow and

2. Captain Angus Cunninghame Graham, Don Roberto's nephew and heir.

3. Tschiffely, A. F. *Don Roberto*. London, Heinemann, 1937.

London to Buenos Aires and Dunedin. As comfortable wearing the costume of the South American gaucho as the robes of a Moroccan sheikh, he was sculpted in both stone and bronze, painted and photographed in countless equestrian poses, sketched with a defiant buttonhole as he stood in the dock at the Old Bailey[4] and later in his garb as a Pentonville convict, and caricatured from such extremes as a member of a political chain-gang to the guise of Don Quixote. Quite by chance, one day in 1987, I came across another likeness.

On a visit to Britain after an absence of many months, we had finished off a long morning's shopping and sightseeing in London with an excellent meal at The Crusting Pipe, an underground restaurant and wine bar in Covent Garden, full of nooks and crannies and upturned barrels. Waiting to pay the bill in the cramped space, I glanced towards the head-high exit and found myself staring at the unmistakable figure, an unnamed subject in a framed satirical cartoon of his turbulent days in the House of Commons, a time immortalised in *Hansard* through his imperious phrase – 'I never withdraw!' Had anyone else recognised him, I wondered, that day... that month... that year? As we emerged into the daylight I felt a warm glow on my face. Possibly the effect of the wine, but perhaps also the good fortune of yet another encounter with Don Roberto.

Was he the God my mother made him, taking her cue from Aimé and Violet Tschiffely as I then took mine from her? He certainly fed her admiration in the last few years of his life, sending her barely decipherable notes and postcards from travels at home and abroad, one accompanied by a brace of grouse. Stored amongst this correspondence I also found a letter from Violet Tschiffely in response to the condolences she had received from my mother while Graham's remains were still en route from the Argentine on the *Almeda Star*. It contained a short but memorable word-picture:

> *I can't bear to think that he will not come into our flat again, fluffing his hair with one hand and in the other a large pot of azaleas or whatever plant was in season.*

The two early biographies of Graham were given pride of place on the bookshelves at Skelbo, our home in Dumbarton. My parents' copy of the first of these, by Herbert West,[5] was inscribed with the characteristic flourish of the subject's own hand and Aimé Tschiffely affectionately autographed his own book for them when it appeared

---

4. Graham was arrested and later imprisoned for six weeks for his involvement in the Irish Home Rule associated Trafalgar Square riots of Sunday, November 13th 1887, referred to at that time as "Bloody Sunday".

5. West, H. F. *Robert Bontine Cunninghame Graham – His Life & Works*. London, Cranley and Day, 1932.

in 1937. It was little short of a total catastrophe for my mother when this very special volume went astray shortly after the war. I described the loss in the correspondence columns of the *Scottish Field* in 1970. My letter was seen by Alexander Maitland, himself the author of a short study on Graham and his wife, and he forwarded a clipping to Violet Tschiffely. By then well into her eighties, she bought a copy of the book from a second-hand dealer in London, sending it to Canada with a signed card in memory of both men. Coincidence, happenstance, or fate? Another privilege, certainly, reinforced by the subsequent arrival of a second book, the personal copy of a complete stranger, an elderly lady living in the North of England.

"R.B.", as my mother always referred to her hero, was apparently delighted with West's portrayal. If he had lived to read Tschiffely's book his reaction would have been equally favourable, for the likelihood is that he aided and abetted both authors, feeding them with material and reminiscences of his own particular choice. As a result both biographies were long in terms of enthusiasm, perhaps, and somewhat short in terms of real scrutiny of worth. Four decades later Cedric Watts and Laurence Davies addressed the task in an entirely different fashion,[6] analysing in depth the influence of his many campaigns and the unjust neglect of his writings, a literary output of close to forty volumes of adventurous travel, history and biography. Their penultimate paragraph re-emphasised yet again that remarkable roll-call, the passionate involvements which led to Graham being categorised, even dismissed by critics as being simply a leader of doomed projects. Just consider them now: social justice for women; an eight hour day and a decent standard of living for working people; free education and freedom of speech; the trade union movement and the Labour Party; the Scottish National Party and Irish Home Rule; and an end to the injustices of British imperialism, a cause he advocated before the end of the nineteenth century. As Watts and Davies concluded:

> *The claim that Graham always supported lost causes is itself a lost cause.*

A fellow Dumbartonian, John Walker, with whom I have corresponded for many years but never met, has worked tirelessly to restore the value of Cunninghame Graham's literary work, reintroducing him to a more modern audience in new volumes of his

---

6. Watts, C. and Davies, L. *Cunninghame Graham – A Critical Biography*. Cambridge, Cambridge University Press, 1979.

cosmopolitan sketches[7] and also through innumerable articles and annotated bibliographies. John made me aware of the term "Grahamophile", a company in which I immediately claimed the right of amateur membership. A monument to Graham was erected at Castlehill on the western outskirts of Dumbarton in 1937, and in one of his articles Walker describes how he used to play in the grassy field round that monument, "the monny" as it was affectionately known to the local children. My brother and I played soccer in that same field, round that same monument. Now relocated to the old Graham estate of Gartmore, to which spot my family and I made a short pilgrimage in 1995, it carries these words:

> *Famous author, traveller and horseman, patriotic Scot, and citizen of the world, as betoken by the stones above. Died in Argentina, interred on Inchmahome. He was a master of life and a King among men.*

Graham's commitment to Scottish nationalism was a lifelong one, for he had joined the Scottish Home Rule Association as early as 1886, the same year he entered Parliament as Liberal MP for West Lanark. He then worked alongside Keir Hardie during the early days of the Socialist movement and although eventually becoming somewhat disillusioned with the Scottish Labour Party, served as its first president. Many years later he accepted a similar position with the fledgling National Party of Scotland, loving to boast that his forebears had fought with Wallace at the Battle of Falkirk in 1298 and never hesitating to rouse an audience by invoking the patriot's name:

> *Wallace is Scotland: he is the symbol of all that is best and purest and truest and most heroic in our national life. You cannot figure to yourselves Scotland without Wallace. He prepared the way, and is preparing the way with your assistance for a National Legislature in Scotland. He is a man whose memory can never die. So long as the grass grows green, or water runs, or whilst the mist curls through the corries of the hills, the memory of Wallace will live.[8]*

---

7.   Walker, J. *The South American Sketches of R. B.Cunninghame Graham*. Norman, University of Oklahoma Press, 1978; Walker, J. *The Scottish Sketches of R. B. Cunninghame Graham*. Edinburgh, Scottish Academic Press, 1982; Walker, J. *The North American Sketches of R. B. Cunninghame Graham*. Edinburgh, Scottish Academic Press, 1986.

8.   Speech given in 1920 during the celebration of Wallace Day.

How fitting was his appointment as the first president of the party now known simply as the SNP?[9] Consider the sentence at the core of Graham's emotional Presidential address at the inaugural meeting of the National Party, held on the anniversary of the Battle of Bannockburn in June 1928:

> *We want a National Scottish Parliament in Edinburgh in order*
> *to deal with Scottish measures under the eye and pressure of a*
> *Scottish electorate.*

While those words required more than seven decades to come full circle, Don Roberto's spirit must have been hovering over Holyrood when the members of Scotland's first Parliament for over 300 years took their seats in Edinburgh in 1999, and watching again surely as Alec Salmond led his SNP colleagues into the debating chamber after their election victory in 2007. With these events showing clearly that the final crusade of a quite extraordinary life was no more of a lost cause than all the rest, perhaps my early assessment of our visitor was not so far off the mark.

In the latest biography of this remarkable man his great niece Jean writes:

> *In 1932 Dr Humble came on regular visits to his friend and patient*
> *at Ardoch. As his car crunched off over the gravel of the front drive*
> *after one of these visits...*[10]

I still remember the crunch of that gravel from accompanying my father on his home visits to the family at Ardoch in later years. Although my career choice was still very much in the future, the never-forgotten medical connection with Don Roberto may well have left its mark.

---

9. Scottish National Party.

10 Cunninghame Graham, J. *Gaucho Laird*. The Long Riders' Guild Press, 2004, p. 365.

THREE TEACHERS

*The student can be taught not only what to learn, but also
how to learn it.*
Dickinson W. Richards

Four years at Merchiston Castle School in Edinburgh gave me an appreciation of many things. Although I had mixed feelings about some aspects of the experience at the time, these have gradually fallen into their proper perspective, leaving an awareness that the school provided an excellent preparation for the realities of life. By any standard the education was a privileged one, and by the same token it remains a privilege to have been there. Today's Merchiston boys travel the world, with countless opportunities which were unavailable to us in the immediate post-war period. We fared pretty well, however, except for the lack of one major facility, the swimming pool added in 1961 as a memorial to the Headmaster of our era, Cecil Evans.

The school's long history goes back as far as 1833, to the founding of the eighty-pupil Merchiston Castle Academy by Charles Chalmers. By the time of my arrival in 1944 the new Colinton site had accommodation for around two hundred boys. Divided into houses according to age, in contrast to the traditional system of the English public schools, we moved into new quarters in the autumn term of each year. Previous all-round success at a small preparatory school did not guarantee its continuation in a larger setting and I found many things at Merchiston very different from Cambusdoon in Ayrshire, where my brother and I had been sent as the threat of war grew in the late 1930s.

The spirit of Merchiston centred on a proud rugby tradition, with sporting prowess impressing one's peers much more than academic achievement. Since an eye condition had deprived me of binocular vision I was denied significant success in games requiring precise hand-to-eye co-ordination, and due to two quite separate illnesses unfortunately missed most of the first half of two successive rugby seasons, never fulfilling whatever minor promise I might have had. My best game may have been my very last. I charged the ball at every opportunity, determined to demonstrate to one particular boy that I could play this game as well or better than he. "Corky" Mair, the rugger coach, came over during lunch in the communal dining room. 'Are you going to be here next year, Humble?' he asked. I told him I was hoping to be accepted into Medicine at Glasgow University during the summer. 'Pity,' came the reply, the nearest I ever came to a try-out for the first fifteen squad.

On the academic side, we had fixed hours for evening study, passed or failed rigidly timed exams, took home critical end-of-term reports and were liable to chastisement by both cane or strap, all anathema to the modern educational expert. I cannot recall any lasting damage from such punishments other than to one's pride. If I suffered difficulties in those days they came principally from the fact that boys who wore glasses were automatically categorised as weaker individuals. It was not always easy to break out of this image or to avoid some inevitable bullying, and although most of us survived these sorts of trials happily enough, I cannot vouch for all. Is not that a mirror image of life?

In terms of their ability to control a classroom of high spirited boys a few of the occupants of the 1944 Common Room[11] left something to be desired, but we were also exposed to some outstanding teaching. Over and over as the years have slipped by I have come to realise the debt I owe to three individuals, to F. A. Rhodes, H. R. Charter and A. H. Humphries, as much for the manner of their teaching as for the subjects they taught.

Going back in memory to our classes in Gibson House in 1944, where Mr Rhodes held his Physics lab, and to struggles over the Wheatstone Bridge, Ohm's Law and the rest, I recall that for one without a natural aptitude for Physics the subject was presented in a simple and practical manner. I hope I may have passed on something of his patience to a few students in succeeding years. There were no special teaching aids in those days, no xeroxed handouts, no calculators or computers, just fundamental knowledge lucidly imparted. "Tommy Farr", as we remember Mr Rhodes better,[12] contributed much to other aspects of life at Merchiston and I can think of no teacher I have met since whose methods were based on sounder principles.

To "Charlie" Charter I owe the instillation of an interest and understanding of organic chemistry. Although I have never been directly involved with chemistry, the simple lessons he passed on continued to be of value in my everyday work. Other images can still be conjured up from quiet sessions at the Chess Club and thankless umpiring duties with the Third and Fourth Cricket Elevens, the latter a graveyard for the less than gifted. He was the umpire on one never-to-be-forgotten occasion when I astonished myself and one or two others by capturing three wickets in four balls. In

---

11. The meeting room shared by all the school's teachers.

12. From his repetitive use of his initials (FAR). Tommy Farr was a boxing idol at that time.

fairness I have to admit that I was bowling at batsmen of a somewhat indeterminate class! Irascible Charlie may have been at times, but gratefully remembered.

What can one say finally about the man we knew as "Humph"? To me he was, and is, Merchiston. As befitted a school whose first premises, Merchiston Tower, had belonged to the family of John Napier, the inventor of logarithms, I could not have had a better Maths teacher. But it is Humph as a person who remains especially unforgettable – his humour, his kindness and fairness in every aspect of life, much of which must have been handed on to literally hundreds and hundreds of boys. It would need a book to even begin to mention the contributions he made to the school, but as we all remember him we can only be grateful for the fates that led us there. Another Merchiston legend, Ian Balfour-Paul, teacher and orraman[13] at the school for over half a century, commented on the extraordinary diversity of Humph's interests and knowledge and described him as a figure symbolic of Everyman. As Housemaster of Rogerson West, where boys spent their final year in the school, he took an interest in all of our future plans, going out of his way to discuss my own choice with my mother at a chance meeting in an Edinburgh pub. I still regard Humph as the ultimate teacher, and can find no better way to finish this memory of him than to use words he himself wrote in relation to the passing of a colleague:

> *Looking back at the years a hundred little episodes and stories recur to remind us of the old faces that will not return, but they are all buried in the heart of Merchiston, which will flourish in the future as in the past, and be a full reward for the lives of those who gave so much devotion to develop generations of schoolboys with the will and how to live for the benefit of others.*

There were teachers of another kind in those years, gods even they seemed as they strode onto the stage above me. At fourteen I could neither sing nor read a single note of music. Feeling that I wanted to learn more about the subject, I asked my parents to let me have piano lessons. They told me that wartime restrictions would make this too difficult. My only other option was to join the school's Music Club. Barely a week after doing so, a notice appeared asking for names of those interested in going to a concert by the Scottish Orchestra. I put my name down, never thinking that I would get a ticket nor that just a few days later I would find myself sitting almost under the nose of conductor Warwick Braithwaite in the very front row of Edinburgh's Usher Hall. Far less did I realise that this would open an early door to a lifetime of pleasure from classical music, the final reason for my appreciation of the years at Merchiston. During the four musical seasons of my sojourn in Edinburgh,

---

13. From the Scots word "orra", meaning extra, odd or left over.

the Scottish Orchestra evolved into the Scottish National Orchestra, with Walter Susskind taking over as Director. Guest conductors came on a regular basis and I was privileged to sit in that same front row on many occasions, literally at the feet of such giants of the conducting world as Barbirolli, Boult, Beecham and Sargent, listening to many famous orchestras and soloists. Whilst I remember cellist Pierre Fournier among the latter particularly, my personal highlight was the annual visit of the Hallé Orchestra from Manchester. Although at that time I was too young to recognise the passion and total involvement which Barbirolli brought to every concert, he mesmerised me at such close range, his dark front locks of hair flapping up and down, a total contrast to the dapper Malcolm Sargent, the showman Beecham or the impassive Boult. Musical gods they were indeed for me in those days, with immortality assured through their many recorded performances.

Barbirolli held pride of place in my musical Valhalla; he also stays particularly in mind because of an unusual medical connection. During a long and totally absorbing interview I was fortunate to watch on black and white television in the late 1960s, he confessed to a lifelong fascination with surgery, recounting how he contrived incognito invitations to hospital operating rooms whilst on tour with the Hallé, the chance of watching Caesarean sections being especially relished. In another interview with Michael Kennedy,[14] which I heard for the first time just this year, he likened the technical knowledge of music of a great conductor to the knowledge of anatomy of a great surgeon. His career choice was set when he was handed a violin at a very early age,[15] but perhaps his alter ego sometimes envisioned a very different world, still at centre stage but with scalpel in hand rather than baton. Just a man, not a god after all!

---

14. R. Holden ed. *Glorious John. A Collection of Sir John Barbirolli's Lectures, Articles, Speeches and Interviews.* The Barbirolli Society, 2007.

15. Becoming exasperated by the boy's habit of playing his violin whilst wandering all over the house, his grandfather anchored him firmly by replacing the smaller instrument with a cello!

THE WRONG CHOICE?

...the world before me, the long brown path leading wher-
ever I choose...
Walt Whitman, from *Song of the Open Road*

Why did I choose medicine as a career? Thinking back to my last two years at school when this sort of decision had to be made, I really couldn't tell you. Did the choice come from the fact that my father and a favourite uncle were both doctors, confirmed perhaps by the former going out of his way to try to persuade me against it? Did the Don Roberto connection play a part? Or was it mainly a backlash against my taking a quite different road, one that might have led me into a position somewhere in the field of history? That option had been placed firmly in my mind by a fourth so well remembered teacher, the man who thrilled me by his approach to history when I was twelve years old. Alas for pedestals, however, and those we place upon them! Some months after leaving Cambusdoon I was shattered to learn that he had been sent to prison for the sexual abuse of a number of boys at my old school, those in the year behind us. Not only that, but he had a prior record of such offences. How close we must have come to similar indignities, for in that last winter and spring in Ayrshire we were regularly invited to his study for small group tutorials. Although his name even disappeared from memory for many years after this crashing fall from grace, his shadow remained, leading me back in later years to the subject he taught so well.

A career counsellor came to the school, I think when I was around seventeen. 'What do you intend to do on leaving school?' he asked. 'Become a doctor,' I replied immediately, 'and then specialise in tropical medicine.' He seemed surprised, but expressed interest. I'm not sure what I said next, for truth to tell the idea of this speciality only came to mind as I had been reading about Patrick Manson's work on malaria that very week. The tropics gave us something to chat about for the remainder of the interview, however, and doubtless he made an entry such as the following: "Humble, R – Medicine – father a doctor – seems well enough motivated." Little did he know. At the time it somehow seemed as though I had no other choice.

And so the die was cast, a minor advantage being that should I be accepted as a medical student at Glasgow University I would be able to postpone the required period of National Service and trade two years of general duty soldiering for a later life as a commissioned officer.[16] With many ex-servicemen returning in the late 1940s the competition for university places was intense and my name was missing from the first list of successful applicants. A phone call from my father to eye specialist Professor Brownlaw Riddell, one of the Entrance Committee members, did the trick. I make no apologies about the string-pulling. After all, I had been the Professor's patient since the age of three!

Just two weeks later, along with two hundred and fifty or so others, I arrived at the old Physics lecture room off Dumbarton Road in the west end of Glasgow to begin the five-year course. It did not take me long to second-guess my chosen career. Dissecting a dogfish was bad enough, but when we moved on to human corpses in second year thoughts of being a private in the Army seemed more like Shangri La! How I loathed those early anatomy sessions and the formalin-pervaded odour one could never escape. I even came to hate the disarticulated limbs which were provided for small groups of students, and couldn't wait to get away from the dissecting room each day. My first "spot" examination proved a total disaster – an ignominious thirteen percent. Surely this must be the wrong choice? Strange to think that in the end I came to enjoy anatomy, even if this turnaround did not take place until years later when I was studying for the primary Fellowship in Anaesthesia. Whatever the early doubts about my profession I have to admit that it has led me all over the world and given me an extraordinarily varied life. Reflecting now on so many different incidents, in so many different places, each one seems to possess its own individual flavour or humour, or to teach its own lesson. And surely there can be no better place to start than at that venerable institution, the old Glasgow Royal Infirmary.

---

16. A rank of Second Lieutenant in the RAMC (Royal Army Medical Corps) was auto-matically given to all National Service doctors, or an equal rank for the few who opted for the Royal Air Force or Navy.

STUDENTS AND DOCTORS
JUST ANOTHER EVENING
ON CALL

He had a broad face and a little round belly,
That shook, when he laughed, like a bowlful of jelly.
Clement C. Moore

My friend Jim and I elected to do our first terms of practical surgery in 1950-51 at the Glasgow Royal Infirmary, under the tutelage of Mr Alfred Clarke. The old Royal had five surgical floors, each of which assumed responsibility for the staffing of the Gatehouse at the Castle Street entrance on a specific day of the week, as well as for all of that day's emergency admissions. A working day in the Gatehouse pretty much reflected the rough and tumble world of Glasgow's east end, the pendulum constantly swinging from trivial conditions to serious emergencies. With family arguments, drunks and violent offenders thrown in, the police never seemed to be absent for long. We were spectators to life in all its variety, including one hilarious incident when a nurse chased an inebriated and trouserless male patient half-way up Castle Street.

We donned half-length white coats and although most patients understood the realities of the situation we were often addressed as 'Doctor'. Our task was to take an initial history and to try to come to a semi-intelligent diagnosis prior to the arrival of a member of the junior surgical staff. Jim ran into difficulties one Tuesday when a young chap in his early twenties refused to co-operate, demanding to talk privately to 'a proper doctor'. He looked totally healthy, and although we speculated on the possible cause for such behaviour we did not come close. The house surgeon took him into a side room, reappearing after a while with a broad grin on his face, a whispered conversation then producing a furious blush on the face of one of the attending nurses. They sent for a variety of instruments, pronouncing after a long delay that the patient would have to be admitted for examination under anaesthesia.

It took a while for the full story to emerge, the unfortunate young man eventually confessing that 'he and a few of the lads had been fooling around'. Fooling around proved something of an understatement. We had heard of stupid pranks with

16

compressed air hoses sometimes ending disastrously, but never of an individual being a willing participant in an encounter with an oversized carrot.

Alfie Clarke only attended his unit's evening emergency lists on the rarest of occasions, but my memory is that he was in the operating theatre[17] that night, merciless in his comments to the great embarrassment of the younger nurses. Whilst one might look askance at such behaviour in today's "enlightened" times, for immature students of medicine and nursing it was actually educational, significantly broadening our experience in the realities of human behaviour. Since no available surgical instrument proved an ideal grasper for the proposed procedure, the extraction of a fourteen-inch carrot from a quite unfamiliar passageway, the removal process was by no means easy, taking at least half an hour. Milking the occasion for all it was worth, Alfie insisted on sending for a measuring tape, claiming it must be a world record! The dimensions having been duly recorded on the chart, we returned to the more mundane world of strangulated hernias and ruptured appendices. Jim and I were supposed to be learning about surgery and this had been just another evening on call.

The following year we moved down two floors to take our second main surgical rotation, attached now to Professor J. G. "Pop" Burton's wards. Pop was something of a legend among Glasgow medical students. Originally a pathologist but by this time a sound although perhaps not outstanding surgeon, he had a physical build to rival Moore's renowned description of St Nicholas. An individualist in every possible way as both a person and a teacher, he never forgot the face and seldom the name of any who passed through his unit. He gave the first surgical tutorial to every group of new students and as we later discovered this followed a time worn pattern, highlighted by the unearthing of an ancient x-ray of the spine. We stared dumbly at the viewing box, totally mystified, for the film was so old and faded that even an experienced radiologist might have needed a microscope to examine it. No one ever spotted the abnormality, of course, so Pop took his usual impish delight in pointing to the hairline fracture of one vertebral body. The punch line followed – it was an x-ray of his own spine – and for what must have been the umpteenth time he launched into the drawn out story of how he had sustained the injury in a famous crash of a troop-train during the First World War. I can't remember learning much about surgery that morning but I have never forgotten the story of the disaster, somewhere in the Carlisle area, down to the numbers of soldiers killed (two hundred and twenty-seven).

---

17. Depending on which side of the Atlantic one works, the following terms are synonymous: Operating Theatre and Operating Room (OR); Operating Department and Operating Room Suite; Ward Sister and Charge Nurse.

Pop had many idiosyncrasies, among them an obsession that no unit other than his own provided clean towels and soap, in consequence of which he travelled the hospital corridors in near-Napoleonic style, with a freshly laundered white towel over his arm and a soap dispenser in his pocket. Seeing him attired in such fashion on the ground floor of the Infirmary one morning, two visiting American surgeons mistook him for a porter and asked to be directed to the Professorial unit. 'Professor Burton's unit? Certainly, sir… follow me, please,' Pop replied, escorting the visitors to the elevator and happily accepting the proffered tip as they exited on the third floor. 'If you wait for one moment, sir, I'll call the Professor.' Needless to say, when the "porter" re-emerged from his office to introduce himself formally to his guests, clad by now in a traditional white coat, the success of the visit was assured. Reputedly the tip was not refunded!

And so our surgical education continued under Pop and his staff, on the third floor of the Royal instead of the fifth and with Wednesdays on call rather than Tuesdays. And if a carrot had been the highlight of all those Tuesdays, it might be appropriate to say that it was topped in the succeeding year by the events of one particular Wednesday. I cannot possibly imagine that any other operating room in the world, before or since, has witnessed such a scene.

Urgent emergencies, such as a not uncommon ruptured ectopic pregnancy or perforated ulcer, went quickly to the operating theatre, while run of the mill cases were admitted to the ward. By nine or ten in the evening two or three of these would usually be lined up. The Royal's surgical wards opened onto a central stairwell area, each floor having its own operating suite off to the north side of the building. This particular evening Jim and I observed the uncomplicated induction of anaesthesia for the first patient, a young man with acute appendicitis, and then helped to wheel the stretcher into the main operating room. Inside, Pop was busy "scrubbing up" at one of two large porcelain sinks, his senior assistant surgeon Mr Murray similarly occupied at the other. It was unusual for a senior surgeon to be the assistant on a relatively minor case such as this, but Pop had his own set of rules. In contrast to the wards, where even as Professor of Surgery he often played second fiddle to the dictates of his senior ward sisters, the operating room remained his exclusive domain.

Each sink was equipped with two elbow taps, one for hot and one for cold water. Hand and arm washing complete, Pop attempted to turn both taps off before donning his sterile gown and gloves. One seemed stuck in the full on position and he directed us to finish the task for him. We found it solidly jammed. With the water still running it soon became apparent that something had blocked the drain. The sink quickly filled to the brim, then began to overflow onto the floor. Since he was no slouch as a surgeon, Pop had already opened the abdominal cavity. He glanced over his shoulder. 'What on earth is going on? Get that damn tap off!'

'It won't budge,' we replied, 'and the drain seems to be blocked.'

We redoubled our efforts as the water began to flow across the room. The theatre porter had a go at the lever, applying all his power at arm's length. Nothing happened. It had stuck, just as completely as the drain had ceased to function. The entire room was soon awash, with the sister-in-charge beginning to lose the place and the appendectomy quickly fading in terms of relative importance. Opening the double doors, we got to work with brushes, sweeping the water out as best we could towards the outside corridor. As the flow continued, it proved a losing battle.

Pop could take it no longer. Ripping off his gloves, he rolled up his sleeves and strode over to tackle the offending tap. He had no more luck than the rest of us. By now the patient was completely forgotten, except perhaps by the anaesthetist, with the operation at a total standstill.

'What are you doing, standing there?' Pop demanded of Mr Murray. 'Make yourself useful! Get a brush and start sweeping.'

Picture the scene for yourself. If scriptwriters had added such a fictional story line to *Doctor in the House*, the film's director would have laughed them out of court. An unconscious patient on the table, with a young scrub nurse immobile and helpless at his side; two medical students killing themselves with laughter as they tried to bale out an operating room; an eminent Professor of Surgery turned plumber; a senior surgeon turned orderly; an experienced sister close to hysterics, her circulating nurse running hither and thither accomplishing precisely nothing; and an elderly anaesthetist vainly trying to remain calm in the midst of chaos. Inured by an often uneasy reception on many previous Wednesdays, perhaps, she made little or no contribution to the very spirited conversation. It seemed like an age before Pop contrived to unblock the drain with an ancient urological instrument. Order thereafter was soon restored, the patient going on to make an uneventful recovery, blissfully ignorant of the mayhem which had surrounded him on the third floor of the Royal.[18] As for Jim and I, this had been just another evening on call, all part of our progress towards membership in a learned profession.

---

18. These stories of Pop Burton were included in an article entitled "First Impressions" which was published in *Today's Anaesthetist* 1999; **14**, 6: 134-135.

A DUBLIN TRADITION

Ring a ring a rosie, as the light declines,
I remember Dublin in the rare ould times
from *Rare Ould Times*, a ballad of Dublin. Peter St John

My memories of Dublin do not go back as far as those of the balladeer, to the haunting rhymes of his childhood, but they come from a time when bicycles outnumbered cars on O'Connell Street, when all the world still met at the foot of Nelson's Pillar, when a month in the city remained within the reach of an impecunious student's budget and from an era not yet blighted by echoes from the North. It was July 1952, and we were participants in a long-standing but now sadly discontinued tradition, the annual pilgrimage across the Irish Sea by fourth year medical students from Glasgow to fulfil the stipulated course of practical obstetrics on "the district". More than thirty years earlier my father had followed the same path, although he took his instruction at Hollis Street rather than at the rival institution to which I was headed, the Rotunda Hospital.

Being the very first city I had visited outside of Britain, Dublin proved something of a revelation, especially the busy O'Connell Street. Overlooked at one end by the brooding statue of Parnell, it had a cosmopolitan and even exciting flavour: the crowded cafés and their never silent jukeboxes; the cyclists weaving in and out between cars with carefree abandon; the Pillar and the Post Office, twin symbols of the old struggles; and at the north end the wide bridge over the Liffey with its confluence of incoming roads, effortlessly presided over by a uniformed magician. We found it all marvellous, learning the basic principles of obstetrics on the way – and much more besides.

Our course stipulated ten home deliveries. We were divided into groups of four, each group containing two "experienced" students who had arrived a fortnight before. Our leader was Dickie Mabon, later to become Member of Parliament for Greenock and a junior minister in the Labour government of Harold Wilson. In obstetric terms I'm not sure whether Dickie knew much more than my friend Alistair and I, but he was outwardly confident and like all true politicians possessed the gift of the gab. It came in useful on one of our early cases. We arrived at a dingy apartment in response to an urgent phone call. The baby, still attached to its mother, was lying face down on the sagging bed in a pool of amniotic fluid. It looked pathetically small and was obviously dead, having apparently made a sudden entry into the world some thirty minutes previously. We ligatured the cord, delivered the afterbirth and generally cleaned things up. Then Dickie astonished me. 'Have you got some holy water?' he asked. A Schweppes tonic water bottle was duly produced, its contents vouched for by the father. 'What name?' our fearless leader continued. And looking as though he did this sort of thing every week, Dickie calmly baptised the unfortunate infant. He then advised the calling of a priest. We were offered a drink, I recall, before departing, but I have no memory as to whether any of the group accepted. I certainly didn't. This sort of thing was quite outside my limited experience. Although we may have exuded some reflected glory from the manner in which the whole affair had been handled, as the junior students in the group Alistair and I were decidedly thankful this was still the first two weeks of our rotation, not the last. We would have been the "seniors" then!

Dr Gault, the "Clinical Clerk" with the unfortunate job of being responsible for all students on the district, seldom failed to emphasise during his lectures just how ignorant we Glasgow trainees were. Reputedly suffering from severe migraines, he always seemed to be in a foul mood, particularly if called on for assistance by the student teams. Being naturally cautious, some groups requested his assistance unnecessarily, causing him to round on us all in withering terms. We therefore tried to avoid involving him, almost at any cost. One particularly long drawn out labour was sweated out, somewhere along Gardner Street – not the most salubrious part of Dublin in those days – with an eventual spontaneous delivery in the persistent occipito-posterior position.[19] The emergence of the baby was something of a revelation to us. In fact we really only put two and two completely together, the unusual appearance of the head and the consequent long labour, on the walk back to the hospital. I have the feeling that our notation of the delivery may have taken some liberties with the truth. We were learning, but it was the long-suffering Irish mothers who were taking most of the risks.

Having cycled, early one morning, to a patient's house about as far from the Rotunda as the groups ever had to go, we managed to gain a fair measure of revenge on Dr Gault. After a quite uneventful delivery the afterbirth refused to co-operate. Although no undue bleeding occurred, we were no further forward an hour later, faced now with the unenviable task of having to call out our tormentor. Since we had been strictly enjoined not to use the telephone unless in a dire emergency, I was despatched by bicycle while the others prepared for a possible manual removal of

---

19. As opposed to the usual occipito-anterior presentation of the baby's head.

the placenta. There was little need to utter the words, for we all realised the situation. I felt better for saying them, however: 'For heaven's sake, have everything ready, and whatever you do, don't let that placenta deliver. We'll never hear the end of it if he has another unnecessary call out.'

The early morning streets were deserted as I broke all speed records back to the hospital. Gault was his usual grim self when called from a deep sleep. Another wasted trip – his thoughts needed no voicing. During the return journey in the van, I kept repeating a silent prayer – 'Don't let that placenta be delivered... please let it still be there.' As we entered the house, the others gave me a hidden thumbs up. No change! Gault put his hand on the abdomen, rubbed up the uterus and made to express the recalcitrant object. Nothing happened. He tried again – still nothing. Muttering under his breath, he began to wash his hands in a basin made ready by my friends. I should explain at this point that there were no pre-powdered gloves in those days. We had been taught to prepare a second basin with boiled water, into which Dettol or some other disinfectant had been added, leaving a pair of fluid-laden gloves in the container, wrists over the edge, ready for the operator to pick up and plunge his hands into rapidly and easily. Gault thrust one confidently into the first glove, immediately letting out a blood-curdling yell: 'Good God Almighty!' [or other more expressive words in the same rough context] 'I'm scarred for life!'

At the sudden sighting of the Rotunda van, my companions had forgotten one very necessary part of the process. They had omitted to add any cold water to the near boiling contents of the bowl. The rest was anti-climax. The patient did require a manual removal of the placenta, which probably saved our bacon, while the operator only suffered a mild scald. Privately we exulted, but I don't imagine he saw the joke. Mark one down for the students in the long annals of the Glasgow-Dublin tradition.

We were shown great respect by the patients. Though they must have known our true status, as in the Gatehouse of the Glasgow Royal, they always referred to us as 'the doctors'. The extent of our comparative ignorance, in practical terms at least, may not always have been apparent to them. Presumably we supervised a number of normal deliveries. Those details have long since disappeared from memory. One further night, however, is well remembered. Dr Gault had a rare evening off and we were managing a labour in what in Glasgow terms would have been called "a single end". The family lived in just one extended room, with a double bed at one end, another smaller one to the side, I think, and a fireplace on the far wall. Mother and father, an uncertain number of kids, and grandmother – all together, even at the scene of yet another arrival. With the four of us it amounted to quite a crowd. Getting near to the end of our month's course, we now had a fair measure of self-confidence. Enough at least to put in a call for help when things started to go wrong, knowing that on this particular occasion our saviour was to be a very different type of individual.

Dr Karl Mullen, Captain of the only Irish rugby team to ever capture the much coveted Grand Slam,[20] was worshipped by Dubliners at large. We "knew'"him well, for Scotland had fared even worse than others at his hands. Hadn't he captained Ireland in victories over us in each of the previous five years, twice at Murrayfield in our presence? Recently retired from rugby and concentrating now on his career in obstetrics, he was the senior of the four Clinical Clerks at the Rotunda. He was also a gentleman, in the true sense of that word, courteous to patients and students alike, and we were privileged to assist him that evening in a forceps delivery under anaesthesia. We had seen a number of these in the labour ward of the hospital, of course, but "the district" raised some different problems. The grandmother refused to leave and under instructions to douse the fire succeeded only in refuelling it further, causing huge flames to roar up the chimney. Although ether and explosions seemed to connect together in our minds, Dr Mullen calmly proceeded with the induction of anaesthesia at the other end of the room, using chloroform brissettes, then switching to open drop ether. Under his direction one of us continued as "anaesthetist", allowing him then to move down to the business end. Some years were to pass before I realised that our fears had been largely groundless, for I witnessed at that time an impressive demonstration by Sir Robert Macintosh, the man who broke new ground as the first ever appointee to a British Chair of Anaesthesia. After showing us how a match could be put harmlessly to the end of glass tubing along which passed a mixture of ether and air, he introduced a minute quantity of oxygen to the circuit. I have never forgotten the brief explosive sound, just as I have never forgotten Karl Mullen. Fortunately we had no oxygen in that crowded flat, and mother and baby did well – as did the four of us, progressing slowly towards our goal of becoming proper doctors.

Those rare old times in Dublin hold other memories: the less than perfect hospital food, with appetites for many often stimulated by a visit to one of the pubs across the street, Conways and Mooneys; our favourite café, The Elite, with the tune of the day, "The Blue Tango", playing constantly; long sessions of bridge while we waited for call-outs; a glorious afternoon on the sands at Portmarnock; and an overnight return by boat to Glasgow, partially frozen on the open decks, with less than two shillings left in my own pocket.

But Jimmy Chapman, another of our student gang, deserves the last word by virtue of his joust with Dublin's famous traffic cop. Speeding across the bridge over the Liffey on his bicycle one day, he noticed that worthy to be absent from his post, standing at the side of the road engaged in an animated conversation with

---

20. Karl Mullen led Ireland to their first Grand Slam in 1948. He died early in 2009, not long after the Irish team had completed a second such triumph after an interval of sixty-one years.

a pedestrian. With no approaching cars to impede him, Jimmy veered to the right across the empty road. There was an imperious blast on the whistle, and an accusing finger: 'And where do you think you're going? Do you not know you have to go round me?'

'How could I go round you when you were standing at the side of the road?' Jimmy mildly replied.

Back came the biting response, accentuated as possible only in the brogue of the speaker: 'Sure you have to go round me whether I'm there or not!'

FOUR MEN IN A CAR

Gaudeamus igitur, Juvenes dum sumus
(Let us then rejoice while we are young).
Medieval student song, traced to 1267,
but revised in the eighteenth century

Medical students who take elective training in anaesthesia today have the chance of a one-on-one preceptorship with an experienced clinician. In addition to receiving a short introduction to anaesthesia they are also exposed to a broad range of other disciplines and skills, making it a course well worth inserting at an early stage into their training. It was not always so. As in all other aspects of medical education, the teaching in my speciality has changed dramatically. Take this experience, for example:

My first giving of an anaesthetic was when, a third-year student, I was called down from the seats and sent in a little side room with a patient and an orderly and told to put the patient to sleep. I knew nothing about the patient whatsoever, merely that a nurse came in and gave the patient a hypodermic injection. I proceeded as best I could under the orderly's directions, and in view of the repeated urgent calls for the patient from the amphitheatre it seemed to be an interminable time for the old man, who kept gagging, to go to sleep. We finally wheeled him in. I can vividly recall just how he looked and the feel of his bedraggled whiskers. The operation was started and at this juncture there was a sudden great gush of fluid from the patient's mouth, most of which he inhaled, and he died. I stood aside, burning with chagrin and remorse. No one paid the slightest attention to me, although I supposed that I had killed the patient. To my perfect amazement I was told it was nothing at all, that I had nothing to do with the man's death, that he had a strangulated hernia and had been vomiting all night anyway, and that sort of

thing happened frequently and I had better forget about it and go
on with the medical school. I went on with the medical school, but
I have never forgotten about it.[21]

This incident occurred in the mid-1890s, the student concerned going on to become one of the legendary figures in medicine, remembered today as the father of neurosurgery. Yet almost sixty years later Harvey Cushing's early experience could still be echoed, albeit in a much more minor way.

In the early 1950s all Glasgow students were required to administer ten anaesthetics under supervision, so Jim and I approached a very well known anaesthetist at the Royal Infirmary one evening as Professor Burton's emergency list was about to begin, showing him the card which he would be required to sign on our behalf. He promptly handed me a syringe, saying: 'There's a good vein in this patient's arm. Put that needle into the vein, and inject the pentothal very slowly.'

My mild observation that I had never even done a venipuncture was brushed aside. To my considerable surprise the needle entered the vein at the first attempt. I began to give the pentothal very slowly, as instructed, watching the speed of injection as though my very life depended on it. I felt pretty pleased with myself, for the option of an intravenous induction was clearly a vast improvement on the open chloroform and ether I remembered from my childhood. A strangled yell from the region of my right shoulder interrupted my reverie, drawing attention to the large swelling which now obscured the front of the patient's elbow. In my attempt to obey the simple instructions I had failed to anchor the syringe, although I had not been warned in any way to take this necessary precaution. Since most of the drug had been injected extravenously, the patient started to complain of severe pain in his arm. I stood back in dismay, watching as the anaesthesia was rapidly induced via the other arm. 'The patient will wake up with an extremely sore arm; it may ulcerate, and he may even lose the limb,' I was told in no uncertain terms.

The operation proceeded in silence. We were given no other comment or instruction of any kind, either on anaesthesia in general or this case in particular. I can still remember my chagrin and remorse, the sleepless night which followed and the daily visits to the ward to see if the limb would survive. To my considerable relief, apart from complaining of significant discomfort for a few days, the patient appeared to come to no lasting harm. As for Jim and I, we were not allowed to help in any way with other anaesthetics in that unit during the remainder of the term, nor given further teaching on the subject. We had to wait until a gynaecology elective in fourth year before being able to fulfil the course requirement, this time under the

---

21. Shephard, D. A. E. 'Harvey Cushing and Anaesthesia.' *Can Anaes Soc J* 1965; **12**, 5: 431-432.

supervision of a friendly individual who was prepared to offer us a modicum of advice. As a result of that early experience, however, the speciality of anaesthesia came very close to last on my list of possible career choices.

How much better to be a medical student at the turn of the twentieth century, one may wonder? With stethoscope around the neck in the required modern fashion, with bedside teaching replaced by the new dogma of 'evidence based medicine' and with eponyms supplanted by acronyms, he or she may well be more knowledgeable than we were at the time of our graduation, or indeed was Harvey Cushing. They spend more time in hospital, too, with no long summer breaks, and have a near certainty of finishing their studies hugely in debt. Whether the combination of all of the above makes them better prepared for the practice of medicine remains open to question.

'Let us then rejoice while we are young' the medieval song goes, but while today's undergraduates can also have opportunities to further their studies in electives around the globe, they may be so busy learning that not enough time is left for rejoicing, or for broadening their experience in many simpler ways. It is amusing to look back to the fact that my first lesson on fractures came whilst I was a general factotum at a private hotel at Machrihanish in Argyllshire. Feeding the chickens formed part of my daily duties and an inadvertent step in their midst resulted in one of them sustaining a cleanly broken leg. A Glasgow surgeon, the late Harry Wapshaw, happened to be one of the guests. We fashioned a more than adequate splint from two rolled-up pages of the local newspaper and "Hopalong", as we christened her, survived to lay many an egg for the hotel's visitors! During two full summers, unpaid apart from board and lodging, I remained totally divorced from medical studies, learning instead how to cope with the idiosyncrasies of diverse groups of hotel guests, how to play mah-jong, how to hit a golf ball into a stiff wind coming off the Atlantic and – back home in Glasgow – the meaning of "ygorra".

Ygorra! A strange word, intelligible now only to an older generation of Glaswegians, or to those who studied at Gilmorehill in bygone days. It can be loosely interpreted as "you've got to" – contribute, that is, to the annual Charities' Day drive which occupied our efforts on one Saturday of each student year. We dressed in a variety of guises, as Indians, sheikhs, policemen and Springbok rugby players, these last outfits in the year when Scotland were annihilated 44-0 by South Africa. This brought us a brief taste of fame, a few lines about four muscular Springboks appearing in a report in the pages of *Punch* magazine. I'm afraid we spent far too much time that year passing a rugby ball around the city streets, our tin cans finishing a great deal lighter than they should have done. Each year brought a new slogan parodied from the Scots tongue, such as "Hannah Ratanner" (hand over a sixpence), "Philup MacCann" (fill up my can) and "Poppa Bobbin" (put a shilling in), and the long-suffering citizens of the city would indulge our high jinks once more as we performed a "Dashing White Sergeant" or "Petronella" down the middle of Sauchiehall Street, long before any part of that famous thoroughfare had become vehicle-free. With today's traffic volumes I can't see such antics going down too well in many civic centres, but we were always received with patience and humour. Charities' Days disappeared a good number of years ago, sadly, swallowed up by the burgeoning numbers of professional charitable organisations. These occasions were symbolic of an earlier and simpler era, however, when "Gaudeamus igitur" really did apply.

One summer, when today's students might be worrying more about tutorials and finances, four of us bought a car. A 1930 Austin Twelve to be precise. It cost us seventy-five pounds and we sold it two months later for sixty five. In the time between we drove down the eastern side of England, across the south to Devon and then back up the west of the country through Shrewsbury to Blackpool and the Lake District, camping as we went. Not everyone welcomed our tents. One farmer refused us permission to camp, simply because we came from Glasgow. He didn't give any specific reason for his low opinion of Glaswegians, but we had to move on. Maybe he didn't like the kilt Alistair was wearing. Another gave us the use of his field but omitted to tell us that his cows came that way to the morning milking. We were awakened by swaying guy ropes, and a horn appearing through a sudden rent in one of the tents. "Decamp" is now a word in the artificial language of modern medical administrators which they employ in the sense of the discharge of patients from hospital. A few years ago I had a long argument with one of them about such usage. We didn't discharge ourselves from our tents that morning, we decamped – in the full and proper meaning of the word!

The old Austin gave us some significant problems. I had considerable difficulty in learning how to double-declutch and must have come close to losing control of the car on a long and twisting descent in Yorkshire, though at the time I refused to acknowledge this possibility to three extremely nervous companions. The dynamo burnt out some days later and then – near Preston – the gear lever came apart in Alistair's hand when he tried to engage a lower gear whilst he and Ronald were returning from a shopping expedition. Jim and I attacked them when they finally arrived back at camp, more than an hour late for supper, only to be totally silenced by the sight of the gear lever being handed through the open window of the car! We made it back to Glasgow in the end, despite these difficulties, managing to conceal the bald tyres and near dead battery from a prospective buyer who wanted the car for a wedding. Whether he got it to the church on time was a matter of little concern to us. We had recouped most of our money.

We let off steam in other ways, too, notably on one special occasion in a banner-and-balloon-strewn Kelvin Hall at the raucous induction of "King" John McCormick, the Scottish Nationalist, as Lord Rector of Glasgow University. Though this position is a largely nominal one, it has a long-standing history and tradition. An ancestor of Don Roberto held the post in the eighteenth century. He himself ran twice, first in 1914 under a Socialist banner and then on a Scottish National platform in 1928, being unsuccessful on both occasions. As a committed crusader for the rights of women, it was ironic that his second defeat came largely as a result of the female undergraduate vote. Most of the women felt obliged to give the better known Stanley Baldwin their support, since he had been responsible for the introduction of universal suffrage in Britain.

It was not all fun in our day, of course, and we had to study pretty hard at times. We also received some excellent teaching from many fine physicians and surgeons, bedside clinicians of the old school. With their help we made it to our final exams. Two personal incidents from that time stand out. A loud shout of laughter on my part in the old Cosmos Cinema in Renfield Street during a showing of *Doctor in the House*, when an examiner asked a candidate in the on-screen "finals" to discuss the signs and symptoms of the condition known as Pink Disease. No one else in the audience had the slightest clue as to the reason for my reaction, but two days before an examiner in Paediatrics had fired the identical question at me. I survived Paediatrics but ran into trouble in Surgery. Feeling that my written paper on that subject had been less than satisfactory, I became exceedingly nervous at the subsequent oral, the two elderly surgeons behind the desk taking on ogre-like appearances. One of them handed me a glass specimen jar, which I almost dropped. My hands shook violently and my mind went totally blank. It might have been a jar of sweets for all I could tell.

'Why are you so nervous, Mr Humble?'

'I don't think I got a good mark in the written, sir.'

They consulted their notes, and talked briefly. 'Well, we thought you did rather well. Put that specimen down on the table before you drop it and tell us what it is.'

'I don't know... I suppose... might... might it be bowel, sir?'

'It might indeed. Which part?'

They then took me slowly through the identification of a classic abscess of the appendix and I weathered the storm. By the end of the oral, rather than ogres, they seemed more like a pair of friendly grandfathers. With less sympathetic examiners I might have been re-sitting surgery in a further six months, rather than celebrating a pass. We graduated on the 4th of July, an appropriate enough day for a start to one's professional career.

The licensing authorities termed the first twelve months after graduation a "pre-registration year". In our case, this took the form of two six-month stints as house surgeon and house physician, the equivalent of a rotating internship in North America. We signed on at Hairmyres Hospital on the outskirts of Glasgow. I knew little of medical history and paid absolutely no attention to its close proximity to Long Calderwood, the birthplace of the famous Hunter brothers.

Although there were many medical and surgical lessons to be learned, it was still a carefree time. The collective effect of a minimal salary tends to bring young people even more together, as happily also did the absence of television as an off-duty distraction. Solo whist, liar dice, and the "Top Twenty" were the alternatives of the day and many lifelong friendships were forged or strengthened. We continued to do some daft things.

One of our number was not universally popular. We suspected him of blatant preference-seeking approaches to the consultants and decided to teach him a lesson he might never forget. When this individual was off duty in Glasgow one day, Bob Robertson – who must have had a better head for heights than I – climbed out from his own second storey bedroom, scrambled along the roof and in again through the open window of our colleague's room. There he proceeded to remove all the screws from the door hinges, returning the door to an apparently locked and secure position before retracing his steps. We awaited the occupant's return with bated breath... the footsteps up the stairs and along the corridor... a seemingly endless pause for the extraction of a key... and then the most almighty clatter and a sound of all hell breaking loose. Fortunately our victim did not injure himself. I doubt if we should have been proud of ourselves but we did savour the moment. It helped to balance the long nights on call and other responsibilities – the evenings and weekends for instance when we were required to be the sole arbitrators of cross-matching blood prior to emergency transfusions. Despite our total lack of experience or proper instruction in this technique, the patients appeared to survive and even thrive – quite astonishing to look back at now when such a practice might bring even a junior physician in front of judge and jury.

Although the erudite Keith Morris was an outstanding teacher and clinician, in practical matters we probably learned as much from the marvellous senior nursing staff as we did from the physicians. And without the "rights" expected by all today we put most inconveniences of the year down to experience, including being shouted at. Some had their own way of dealing with this particular problem.

One morning John Styles was assisting a surgeon who found refuge from the stresses of surgical difficulties in a continual tirade against the junior members of the operating team. Pulling with all his strength on two large surgical retractors in an attempt to provide adequate exposure of an operative site deep in the pelvis, John found himself being urged to the impossible: 'Swab, dammit, man, swab! I can't see a thing! Why can't you keep the wound clear... swab, dammit...'

The "man" quietly laid down the retractors. 'Look, sir, if you want me to hold one of these retractors in my teeth, please say so. I might then be able to swab with one or other of my remaining hands.'

The operation continued – and was completed – in total silence, and there were fewer complaints in succeeding weeks. Our year ended with a flourish, a party for the senior medical and nursing staff, with the liquid refreshment highlighted by a concoction of uncertain alcoholic origin, which we christened "Silent Coronary". The senior surgeon, the late Ken Macrossan, had only just returned to work following a severe heart attack. He turned a little pale on reading the name beside the punch bowl but entered into the spirit of the occasion along with everyone else, enjoying with them our rendition of a hastily composed Hairmyres song. Containing a verse about each of our group, it was sung to the tune of "The Garden Where the Praties Grow", and had the following chorus:

> *Oh, we're the boys of old Hairmyres you hear so much about,*
> *The people stop and stare at us whenever we go out;*
> *They wonder why we look so well, they've heard about our meals;*
> *They know we get the garbage from all the local fields!*

Good food or bad, it was time to move on. Further hospital appointments for some, entry into speciality training or family practice for others, particularly the older ex-service members of the year, and the compulsory two years of National Service in the Army for the rest of us. I never had any intent at the time other than to become a general practitioner.[22] I had a role model, too, in this objective, a man whom I came to know much better than my own father, a man all referred to simply as "The Doctor".

---

22. A traditional British term, otherwise family doctor or family physician.

THE DOCTOR

*There are men and classes of men that stand above the
common herd
...the physician almost as a rule.*
Robert Louis Stevenson

In the dedication to his book *Underwoods* Stevenson discusses the qualities which he most admired in the many physicians he had known. These qualities can be embodied in a single word, its meaning often raised nowadays when talk turns to the medical profession. The word is *trust*. How has such trust come to be questioned? Is it the fault of the profession, or can the blame be laid at the door of our society? The truth of the matter is that both have changed.

My father's younger brother, John, who worked as a much loved and respected family doctor in East Molesey for forty-five years, was a physician of the old school. The profession of medicine dominated every aspect of life at The Hollies on Palace Road, with the household run by his wife Jean in total subservience to the needs of the practice. Although both morning and evening surgeries were held at the house, visitors and patients rarely heard mention of the name Dr Humble. Rather it was 'Has The Doctor finished his bath?' (a morning ritual), 'Does The Doctor still have patients in the waiting room?', 'I'm sorry, The Doctor is out on his rounds' or 'Can I speak to The Doctor?' – an honoured title, but also an inherited one.

John Humble, sixth in a family of eight brothers, graduated in Medicine at Glasgow University and came to East Molesey in 1927, close to Hampton Court Palace and the River Thames. When he arrived to be interviewed for the assistant's position in the practice, the procedure did not quite follow the pattern he had anticipated. He was told that "The Doctor" was out on his rounds. The interview, conducted solely by that individual's wife, took the form of a long social conversation over tea during which medicine was barely mentioned. Dr Knox did not appear on the scene until shortly before the time of the return train to London, his part in the proceedings being limited to enquiring firstly if John could ride a horse, or might be prepared to learn immediately, and secondly when would he be able to start work?

32

While his possession of a Diploma in Public Health may have helped, conversational and riding skills were apparently the matters of primary importance – the ability to deal with medical problems could always be developed on the job!

As John had never been on a horse in his life he took lessons after each evening's surgery, beginning almost four decades of service as Medical Officer to Hurst Park Racecourse. During any hurdle race or steeplechase he was required to ride to the centre of the course, waiting there for indications of problems with a fallen rider. He laughed when telling me about some of his early experiences:

> 'The first few times I was petrified. But Kitty the mare knew more about what was going on than I did and I needn't have worried. Each time the ambulance started up, Kitty immediately followed; I just sat still and went with her. I only came off once, much later, on a different horse, Bess. Startled by the shouts of the crowd, she swerved one way while I went the other. Fortunately I managed to hold onto the reins. Another time Bess and I were cantering near the stands when we were overtaken by a riderless horse. Bess immediately quickened towards the finishing post and the bookies started the crowd cheering with the call of "two to one The Doctor".'

All the famous British jockeys of the pre- and post-war eras rode at Hurst Park. John knew them all, including the legendary Steve Donaghue, Charlie Smirke, Gordon Richards, Harry Wragg, Fred Winter and Lester Piggott. Everyone imagined that he must have received lots of tips from the jockeys over the years, but such was not the case:

> 'There were never any tips – well, perhaps one. Gordon Richards came in one day in the days before his Knighthood, with a speck of dirt in his eye. "Any good tips for today, Gordon?" I asked. "Yes, Doctor," he replied, "I've five more rides to go, and I won't win on any of them." And he didn't!'

Lester Piggott, who took over the mantle of Sir Gordon in later years, failed to report on one occasion as all jockeys were required to do following any fall, refusing to come to the first aid room and simply saying that he was fine. When the Clerk of the Course came to check on his condition John told him that Piggott had refused to be examined. Following an enquiry, which John had to attend, Lester was suspended from riding for the rest of the day.

Many of the jumpers were ridden by wealthy amateurs. Lord Willoughby de Deresby and Captain Sassoon were two who were often injured. Sassoon was well known for his recklessness, eventually being killed in a riding accident. John recalled that the first aid men used to joke that he would always say after a fall, 'Where are my bloody glasses? I can't see.' They reckoned he couldn't see properly even with his glasses on and that was why he came off so often! But in the close to four decades until developers turned most of Hurst Park from a racing circuit into a housing estate, there was only one really serious accident. The story of this incident illustrates just how much has changed in the management of major trauma. One of the prominent riders of the day sustained a fracture-dislocation of the spine and was left paralysed. He was taken to the little two-bedded hospital close to Hurst Park for x-rays and nursed there for ten days, with daily visits by a specialist from London, a regime for a critically injured patient not then considered unusual. With the jockey booked to ride the favourite in the Grand National a few weeks later, they were inundated by telephone calls and direct enquiries.

In the early days the practice found itself rudderless for part of just one day each year, Derby Day at Epsom. The pattern was time honoured. A horse-drawn coach used to stand outside Hampton Court Railway Station where the taxis turn in today. The locals said that the coach owner, Mr Spicer, had to rest the animal for several days ahead of the occasion in order to build its strength for the coming journey! Lunch baskets and champagne were loaded aboard early, with Mrs Knox and John heading off for the Epsom Downs in mid-morning, Dr Knox joining them by car in the early afternoon.

They spread their rugs at exactly the same spot each year, on the inside of the course just beyond the mile post, where the horses flashed by on the way down the hill to the famous Tattenham Corner. Before the introduction of race commentaries on BBC radio the results often took a long time to reach their location, with the occasional fly-by-night bookie disappearing with his take before unfortunate customers arrived to claim their winnings. In the first year after Dr Knox's untimely death John decided only at the last minute to maintain the Derby tradition. It could never be a total day out, however, as they always had to make their way off the course before the last race. Cancellation of the evening surgery was never an option.

Knowing his love of steeplechasing, I once asked him if he had ever been to the Grand National at Aintree. His response was typical. Liverpool was too far away. It would have meant neglecting the practice for too long. In these days when many in Canada cannot even find a family doctor, when wait times in hospital emergency rooms around the world are steadily increasing, and sadly when notices of "one complaint per visit" have started to appear in waiting rooms, such a comment gives much food for thought.

With no capital of any kind to his name when he went into practice, John couldn't afford a car, so his rounds were made on a bicycle with a medical bag tied to the back-carrier. The bike was stolen on his very first house call and eventually the

Knox family lent him a motorcycle and sidecar. When his parents came down from Scotland on holiday two years later, his father accompanied him on visits to patients' homes, sitting in the sidecar. It didn't take long for this comment to be made:

'It isn't quite the thing, John, you know, for a doctor to be doing his rounds on a motorbike. I think I should give you a loan to buy a car.'

And so John bought his first car, a seven-horsepower open two-seater Renault, with a dickey-seat at the back. He loved to talk about the early days of motoring, particularly of driving in the north of Scotland. I am fortunate in having had him record some memories of these mostly forgotten times, journeys when radiators were constantly on the boil, with a receptacle for fetching water from any nearby burn as essential an item of equipment as a crank-handle. Can we imagine today that it was ever necessary to drive a car backwards up a long, steep and twisting ascent? The summit of some hills could simply not be reached in the lowest forward gear: 'Reversing up the old Rest and Be Thankful road beyond Arrochar was bad enough, but having to turn my cumbersome old Morgan on the narrow road before resuming the journey – that was probably even more difficult!'

Single-width roads were very common, particularly in the north, with very infrequent passing spots; some were so narrow that even oncoming cyclists had to back up to such places. John told me of one horrendous late night journey in Sutherland. Arriving with his father in Durness at two am after a totally exhausting sixty-mile drive round Loch Eriboll, they were informed that they must be quite mad. That part of the road towards Cape Wrath had been closed for almost forty-eight hours!

The Queen's long time Racing Manager, Captain Charles Moore, became one of John's patients. Moore lived in retirement in one of the grace-and-favour apartments down by the towpath at Hampton Court Palace. When he developed a viral pneumonia on one occasion, with only a cleaning lady coming in to the house from time to time, John was not satisfied he was being properly attended to. He suggested to Captain Moore that he would be better off in a hospital bed. As the patient refused to contemplate such a suggestion, "The Doctor" decided to enlist an ally. He had known the Queen's physician, Lord Evans, since the time before his peerage when he had been called in as a consultant to see John's critically ill son. Knowing that Evans was coming down to Hurst Park races he phoned him in London. An unusual consultation followed:

'Lord Evans had brought his binoculars for the racing, but no stethoscope. He borrowed mine and took a very cursory listen to Captain Moore's chest. "I think you would be better off in hospital," he said immediately, just as we had decided in advance. "I'm fine where I am, my Lord" was the patient's immediate response. "Humble is looking after me very well here."'

Lord Evans then played his trump card:

> 'I was talking to the Queen this morning, Moore. She is worried about you. Her Majesty agrees with me that you would be better off in hospital.'

The patient was admitted within an hour!

The size of the East Molesey practice grew steadily over the years, particularly after the war. With the number of partners also increasing younger assistants were expected to earn their positions from the start, as his successor Kenneth Brown recalled for me:

> *When I first arrived in the practice at East Molesey in 1960, it was very much a case of being thrown in at the deep end – very different from the gentle and lengthy introduction of today's entrants into general practice. After taking all day to drive down from Glasgow, mostly on the A1 as there were no motorways at that time, I found that I was expected to take my first surgery at 8.30am the following morning – without any introduction whatsoever. I bought a map to help find my way around the town for my visits and just got on with it. Doctor Humble suggested that in order to get to know the patients I should be on duty every second Saturday and Sunday, although there were four other partners. When another new boy arrived he and I were on every third weekend. Can you imagine today's young doctors (and their wives) putting up with that?*
>
> *Dr Humble had been responsible for almost all of the administration in the practice for many years, as neither Tom Bowling or Percy Roger were in any way interested, and his wife Jean looked after all the finances and paid the few staff we employed. This made him a bit autocratic, and eventually we had to insist on minutes being taken at our practice meetings. Otherwise what tended to happen was that although something would be discussed and agreed, John would go home and talk it over with Jean and by the next time we met everything would have been changed!*
>
> *But he was a great fighter for the things that he thought important, such as the Molesey Hospital when it was threatened with closure in the 1960s, and was a very tenacious and stubborn adversary. Medicine was his life, and other than annual visits to Twickenham or Murrayfield he had few outside interests, especially after the racing at Hurst Park finished. He rarely took his*

full holiday allowance in later years, often arranging time off at the last minute and rather grudgingly. He was the archetypical old family doctor, but kept himself well up to date and remained very astute clinically.

He was cautious but not negative about change. Moving out of the surgeries in our own homes and into a central surgery was a major change. We gave him the first choice from the consulting rooms in the new premises, but he did not move in until satisfied that the whole process was going to be a success.

I have great respect for the standards and dedication of John Humble's generation of doctors. The politicians who have forced medicine to become a market rather than a service do not understand what they have destroyed. With everything reduced to its monetary value, there has been a sea change in the attitude of doctors and even nurses. They are much harder, more interested in themselves and less concerned about their patients.[23]

As these comments confirm, any comparison between medical practice in the 1930s and the present time is impossible, for the doctor-patient relationship has undergone a radical change. Service to patients was paramount in the earlier era. Individual physicians made themselves available whenever possible, and for the most part such dedication was greatly appreciated. Patients were treated on a much more personal basis, particularly the private ones, their entire history known to the family doctor who might often deliver a second generation of babies in the same house. Kenneth confirmed for me that his senior colleague managed to keep well up to date in later years, remembering everything about his patients and often putting his finger on things others had missed, while John himself told me stories of the many other roles that had to be filled in the pre-war days.

As well as family confidant, the GP might be called on as the obstetrician, capable of conducting complicated deliveries at home; as the anaesthetist, as comfortable at the head of a labouring woman as at the delivery end; and as occasional surgeon and regular surgical assistant. I naturally questioned him closely about the administration of open drop ether and chloroform to patients lying on old and sagging mattresses, and of forceps and breech extractions under these conditions. In spite of the typically understated reply, 'We never had any problems,' there must have been a few hair-raising moments over the years.

There could be a humorous side to home deliveries in those days. The story of one of John's contemporaries, a family doctor in Dumbarton, is typical. Known locally

23. K. A. C. Brown, personal communication.

as "the late Dr Harvey" because of his propensity for arriving late for almost every consultation or appointment, George Harvey entered the front door of his house one day just as the phone started to ring. It was the local midwife, Mrs Gordon: 'Come quick, Doctor, I've got a breech coming!'

For once in his life George did not delay, not even laying down his hat before making the short journey down the street to a nearby tenement building, arriving just in time to see the crowning of the baby's head. He said nothing until the midwife had completed the totally normal delivery.

'I thought you said it was a breech presentation, Mrs Gordon?'

'Oh, man, Doctor, so it wis! But as soon as I pit doon the phone, the wain gied wan burl and came oot by the heid!'[24]

The words of Robert Louis Stevenson may seem dated now to some, but by the same token they reflect the change in outlook since the nineteenth century. John Humble was not perfect, for he could be stubborn and inflexible, even irritable at times if anything unexpectedly disrupted his set routine, but he earned and retained the trust of his patients and although he may have made no major scientific contributions his fifty years in medicine remain as an example for today's physicians to reflect on.

He retired in 1973 at the age of seventy-two, managing to keep up with the medical literature until his eyesight began to fail and leaving some perceptive comments about kidney disease in the correspondence columns of the *British Medical Journal*. Another abridged letter in the same journal gives us a glimpse of his continuing sense of humour, appearing under the heading, "A conglomeration of containers":

> *The letter from Mr I.D. Fraser reminds me of an occasion soon after the war, when whisky was very difficult to obtain as it was mostly reserved for export. A patient of mine apologised for not bringing a urine specimen I had asked for. The reason was this. The only container which she could find was an empty bottle which had contained Haig's whisky and which still had the label attached. She filled this bottle with her specimen, put it unwrapped in a carrier basket on the handlebars of her bicycle and set off for the surgery. On the way she stopped at the local chemist's shop. When she came out a few moments later her bottle had gone. Unfortunately, neither my patient nor myself ever heard the end of the story!*

---

24. The child gave one sudden turn (or twist) and came out by the head!

Despite regular visits from friends and neighbours and the faithful attention of his sister-in-law Nan, his life held many frustrations in the years following the death of his wife Jean when he became increasingly hampered by blindness. His care towards the end proved entirely fitting, for in a reversal of roles it came at the hands of the staff at the small hospital in Molesey he had served so well. I flew over from Canada for his funeral in January 1985 and for a number of reasons found it a very trying time.

I admired my uncle immensely. As a young child I imagined him as living with my aunt in a very special place, far away to the South. They made occasional appearances during a few of our pre-war summer holidays on the Moray Firth and when talk between him and my father turned to horses, their mention of names like Brown Jack, Easter Hero and Windsor Lad kindled a fascination for me that has lasted a lifetime. One Hogmanay evening when I was twelve he entered my life in a more concrete fashion. Although over the normal age limit, he had volunteered for service in the Royal Navy in 1941. After less than a year at the Colombo naval base in Ceylon the severe illness of his son forced him to accept a compassionate posting home. His ship arrived at the "Tail of the Bank" anchorage on the River Clyde on the 31st of December 1942, and I can still visualise my parents' great excitement when they discovered that he would be our "first foot" for the New Year. My father had a difficult journey round to Gourock in the blackout to pick him up, being stopped and questioned more than once on the way and allowed to proceed only after the production of his special driving permit. They finally got back to Dumbarton around two in the morning. John woke up my brother Graham and me to present each of us with a watch. I remember the occasion fondly as one of the highlights of my pre-teenage years.

A joint passion for racing underlined our friendship as I grew older, and there were frequent visits on both sides of the Border and many shared times to look back on. The incomparable Keith Miller[25] in full flow during a Test Match at Lords; Yehudi Menuhin in his prime at a concert in the Albert Hall; the legendary chaser Arkle measuring his fences and coming up the hill at Sandown Park; meals in countless restaurants where John always declined to accept anything less than the best of food and service; and the great support he provided me following the sudden death of my father in 1953. His adolescence had been spent in Bellfield, Dumbarton, the house where I was born, so our family ties were strong. In broad ranging discussions over the years, whether in direct conversation or by telephone or latterly through the use of cassette tapes, we seldom found that our views diverged, whatever the topic, least

---

25. Quite incredibly in my view, in compiling a roll of the top fifty cricketers of the twentieth century one international panel of experts failed to cast even one vote for Keith Miller.

of all in our shared concerns over the profound changes in modern medicine and the wastefulness of its top-heavy bureaucracy. Included also in those talks were always the annual ups and downs of English cricket and of Scottish soccer and rugby. Rugby remained a special interest. He had proposed marriage to Jean at a Murrayfield international and with a sporting memory developed as a schoolboy in Dumbarton could readily recall the details of many outstanding games, the greatest performance in his mind being that of the Scottish stand-off, Wilson Shaw, in the Calcutta Cup match against England in 1938 which brought Scotland the Triple Crown.

With the regular pattern of its existence unchanged from year to year, The Hollies afforded me the stability I lacked during my globe-trotting years: the immaculate garden with its fine standard roses; the wonderful Gilbert Holiday painting on the wall of the lounge, so evocative of all that is best in the world of horse racing; early evening conversations over sherry or cocktails with Jean's brother, Jack, and his wife Nan, arranged soon after each and every one of my many arrivals; short walks up Palace Road with a succession of admirably trained Bedlington Terriers… Peggy, Punch, Peter and finally Piper; and the practice, always the practice, with concern for patients quietly dominating every waking hour.

I knew that my uncle had not been particularly happy towards the end, still missing even then the contact and friendship of his patients. More than once he expressed his sorrow to me that younger colleagues seldom called on him after he had retired, or even popped in to see him when he became a patient in his old hospital. Deep down I'm sure he felt that his contribution to the community had been largely forgotten, more poignant to think on today since this had been based on what would now be regarded as an old-fashioned idea of service.

The day of his funeral underlined this fact. It was grey and overcast, and ultimately raining, a 'gey dreich day' in Scottish parlance, attended by only a limited number of friends and family members. A top-hatted undertaker walked slowly in front of the hearse as the small cortege left The Hollies and drove down Palace Road. We turned left towards East Molesey's busy roundabout, with the bridge over the Thames coming into view, the road he took so often to Hampton Court Palace and the old Mitre Hotel. In the past John would have been acknowledged here by all. Now few seemed to spare a glance, the old custom of doffing a cap or hat largely forgotten. I felt an inward sense of protest as we left the familiar confines of the village and moved out onto the anonymity of the busy Esher bypass. "The Doctor" had given the best years of his life to the district. As he left on his last journey, hardly a soul remained to say thanks.

SAND AND SERVICE
CAIRO AND THE PYRAMIDS

Pyramids are just as useless! They stay in the desert,
for jackals to make use of and the bourgeoisie to climb.
adapted from Gustave Flaubert (1821-1880)

Although the eighteen months of National Service in the Army which I spent in North Africa had a profound effect on the course of my life, the posting was not exactly the one I had wanted. Towards the end of our six weeks of indoctrination at Crookham, near Aldershot, where a long-suffering sergeant-major tried to turn a group of less than willing young doctors into something resembling army officers, we were asked to list our first three preferences for postings at home or abroad. Why they bothered to go through this supposedly democratic process I'm not quite sure. I opted for East Africa where my mother and brother were living by this time, and was given the Middle East, while a friend asking for Germany soon found himself on his way to Nairobi. I consoled myself with the fact that I was going overseas for the first time in my life, and by the time we had completed further short periods at the Medical Officers' College, Mytchett and the London School of Tropical Medicine and Hygiene I was more or less attuned to the idea of spending two years surrounded by sand. Mytchett stays in the memory largely because of an afternoon's duty at the Farnborough Air Show and a flyover by the ill-fated Comet, while in the big city we probably paid more attention to the shapes of the girls in the Windmill Theatre chorus than we did to the problems of sleeping sickness and malaria.

I never did have a good stomach for travel. Rolling through the Bay of Biscay in a troopship for what seemed like an eternity brought me to a point where I would almost have been happier to die. In the end we made it through the Straits of Gibraltar to the total calm of the Mediterranean. A week spent mainly at the bridge table soon restored our spirits, the ship's Welsh medical officer and I making money steadily at the expense of two regular army officers who stubbornly refused to contemplate any rotation of the partnerships.

41

Our arrival at Alexandria was unforgettable. An armada of small craft surrounded the ship, their owners showing off a myriad of wares, intent on sales at almost any price. Whilst sampling the local Egyptian beer at a sidewalk table following disembarkation we were accosted by a sleight-of-hand artist. He possessed the gift of the gab any Irishman might have envied, persuading us in a trice to place some coins on the table, even a pound note as I recall. We began to understand the meaning of the term "gully-gully man". Threatening him with the police, we beat a hasty retreat while our pockets were still intact – quite a welcome to the mysterious East.

I'm not sure what I had expected of the Canal Zone, but there really wasn't much of anything other than sand. As far as the actual canal went, one rarely saw more than the funnels of passing ships or the sail-tops of larger dhows. Sand pervaded and covered everything else. I spent the first few days near Ismailia doing little other than gazing at it through the flaps of my tent, making occasional trips by Land Rover to the main army base at Fayid. The vehicles always carried an armed escort as Egypt and Britain were at loggerheads at the time and most civilian areas out of bounds. Although the powers-that-be didn't seem to know what to do with me for a while, I was eventually allocated as a general duty medical officer to 2 Field Ambulance whose camp lay just outside of the city of Suez at the southern end of the canal.

Our days were occupied by very routine sick parades, the care of a few bedridden but not particularly ill soldiers, and by the occasional desert exercise. Sessions of bridge and listening to the BBC Overseas Service on battery-powered radios took care of the evenings. Two incidents from that short Egyptian interlude are worth recording. Supplies of toilet paper for the entire British garrison in the Middle East dried up totally for a number of days, a quartermaster's nightmare, and a member of the East African Pioneer Corps died in hospital in Fayid after receiving information that a witch-doctor in his home country had placed a curse on him – this despite the desperate efforts of every available medical specialist in the region. They hadn't told us how to deal with that sort of case during our course on tropical medicine in London.

After three months of the continual taste of sand we were happy early in the New Year to hear rumours that our unit might be moved to Cyprus, trouble-free at that time and regarded as the plum posting in the Middle East. The prospect of a return to comparative civilisation held great appeal and with a successful end to the latest round of political squabbling between Britain and Egypt we were also delighted to learn that the tourist spots were no longer off limits. We made our plans accordingly. Cairo, the Pyramids and the Sphinx; what a weekend to look forward to. Or so I thought. The best laid plans of mice and men… on the Wednesday I was called into the Colonel's tent:

'You've been posted to Tripoli, Humble. I'm sorry to lose you. They keep doing this to me, taking my best chaps away.'

Paying little attention to the "compliment", for Eli Donaldson was well known to apply this description to all of his officers, especially when they were transferred elsewhere, I tried to keep the delight out of my voice. Tripoli was quite as acceptable as Cyprus and that move wasn't even definite.

'When do I have to go, sir?'

'Tomorrow! They need you right away. Their staff is depleted and one medical officer has had to return to the UK on compassionate leave. We'll get the flight fixed up this afternoon.'

'But... but... I'm going to Cairo this weekend, sir. Surely they can wait for me until the beginning of the week?'

'No chance, Humble. I'm afraid they want you immediately.'

Less than twenty-four hours later I was on a DC 3 en route for Tripoli, with stops at Tobruk and Benghazi. We were tossed all over the place in the old Dakota, almost as much in the turbulent air as our ship had been on the waves of the Bay of Biscay, and I was forced to resort to the humiliation of a paper bag. It seemed like a million miles to Tripoli. I can remember taking a long, thankful breath of the unfamiliar humid air as my feet re-encountered solid ground. Viewed through biased National Service eyes, my subsequent welcome at the British Military Hospital was typical of the way the Army often seemed to be run:

'Humble... Humble. Oh, yes... glad you're here, old chap, but we weren't expecting you until some time next week!'

As for the Pyramids, I had to wait close to half a century before the chance of seeing them came round again.

AN IRREVERENT VIEW
OF THE ARMY

'A soldier's life is terrible hard,' says Alice.
A. A. Milne

Given a glimpse of the life of a medical officer in Tripoli in 1955, Alice might have reconsidered her famous comment to Christopher Robin. The only terrible part was the early start to my day. As a nanny she would have taken such hours for granted.

Being short one company, 2 Field Engineer Regiment did not qualify for a resident medical officer and I had the good fortune of being permitted to live in the very relaxed surroundings of the Officers' Mess at the British Military Hospital. Breakfast was served to me by our Libyan servant before any of my companions had stirred and shortly thereafter a jeep arrived to take me across the city for the morning sick parade at the barracks occupied by the Engineers.

My work was normally finished by ten o'clock. Except for regular duty days at the hospital or the occasional exercise in the desert with the Regiment I usually made it to the beach by noon, meeting up there with the other junior Army doctors and their families. There we swam, lazed and picnicked together, debating all the world's problems until around four pm each day. Afterwards we might tackle the challenging nine-hole golf course set in the trees of the hospital grounds, those of us living in the Officers' Mess then settling in after dinner to further rubbers of bridge – often until midnight or beyond. A soldier's life is terrible hard!

I soon learned how to cope with bed bugs and mosquitoes, one's first encounter with a dive-bombing insect inside a mosquito net being quite an experience. Shish kebabs and spaghetti which didn't come from a tin, neither of which were staple items of diet in Glasgow, were equally new, as were the occasional quirks of weather in the form of sandstorms and golf-ball-sized hailstones. In those pre-Gaddafi days one could wander in comparative safety through the Suk, the old Arab market in the heart of Tripoli, and thence along the harbour wall under the shadows of the columns of Romulus and Remus and the Tripoli Ship. We gambled regularly at the

Casino, and drove one weekend through the irrigated orange and olive groves of the country's coastal strip and up the Jebel mountain range to view the famous Lady of Garian. This wartime artist's map of North Africa takes the form of a naked and curvaceous female, of great appeal to a bunch of bachelors. All this and an introduction to archaeology soon to come, not forgetting the many opportunities to take a very irreverent approach to the Army.

I remember a Colonel from Middle East Command, a pathologist I think, who was not at all impressed with our behaviour. Finding us playing bridge in our swimming trunks one evening, he lodged an official complaint with our Commanding Officer. Did this classify as conduct prejudicial to good military order and discipline, we wondered? During the hottest Libyan season of the year the temperature was still around a hundred degrees, with unbearable humidity, yet he considered we should be attired in shirts and slacks, with ties certainly for dinner. He quickly declined the option of eating with us, preferring to try one of the numerous Tripoli restaurants. There he got much more than he had bargained for, a sudden and particularly violent form of food poisoning which had him up and down all night. Trying to catch some brief moments of sleep between the necessary urges, he found an additional hazard. Our mess corporal, a broad-accented Glaswegian named Tortelano, had unknowingly issued him with a mosquito net infested with bed bugs. I hate to think what his report may have said when he returned to the Canal Zone. We were given a mild rebuke by Colonel Dunkerton, our Commanding Officer, but didn't change our habits!

The Army Lists, as sacrosanct as standing orders, were the object of our constant derision. They represented the military bureaucracy against which we railed. In the long history of the British Army I very much doubt if any group of officers has ever deliberately destroyed them. We did more than that. Returning from an excellent meal at our favourite Italian restaurant and no doubt well fortified by its best Chianti, we raided the administrative offices and removed the two large red volumes. I still have the photograph of the ceremonial bonfire we lit, a court martial offence if ever there was one. Looking at the faces of the eleven individuals gathered just outside our living quarters, three married couples and five bachelors, I can make a fair guess as to the identity of the ringleader, whose love of bird-watching in Australia has now overtaken his talent for surgery. Although Bill Liston and Jim Allen from the group have recently died, a bond was forged that night which has lasted for over fifty years. Did they wonder about their missing Army Lists, or did anyone ever actually read them?

Life could never be dull with Bill Liston in one's midst. The sole Irishman in our group and a few years older than the rest of us, his soul-searching medical conscience and penchant for contentious argument enlivened our every waking hour. As a medical student he had driven his car over the quay and into the harbour of an

Irish seaside town. After a social evening out he almost went one better in Tripoli. Returning to the hospital in his Morris Minor, with his wife Ruth in the front passenger seat and two of us bachelors in the back, he approached the large wrought-iron gates. One half-gate was always kept firmly closed, making a stop necessary. Bill's mood overrode such a minor detail. To our dismay he elected to test the width of the other half of the entrance, confidently driving through the opening at what seemed to be around forty miles per hour. We measured it, and the car, the next day. Barely an inch remained to spare on either side! Bill and Ruth's limitless capacity for maintaining close friendships – at both short and long range – became the prime mover in keeping our subsequently widely scattered group in touch.

Those two years gave us the best of both worlds. As physicians quite uncommitted to service discipline we were permitted to practise our profession without too much interference as long as we stayed more or less within the rules. We actually did our fair share of work, for we had to deal with two separate epidemics, first of polio and then of hepatitis. Other challenges came from conditions that medical school had skimped on. I learned a lot about skin and ear problems, and encountered my first cases of venereal disease, a marvellous overall introduction to general practice with patients who were all fit young adults. With the help of an excellent book which I had received from "The Doctor" prior to leaving for the Middle East I also learned that one could work wonders with some advice on basic hygiene and a few simple prescriptions. Although I briefly considered radiology as a possible career choice at this time, family practice was still my aim. The death of a young child under anaesthesia in the operating room at BMH Tripoli towards the end of my time there did nothing to increase my continuing low level of interest in that particular speciality.

My companions also had to cope with the dead and badly injured from a BOAC plane which plunged into an orange grove on the outskirts of Tripoli. I was home on leave at the time, due to return on a Wednesday by one of three regularly scheduled weekly flights. My brother and I arrived in London on the Monday afternoon to find the evening papers full of the crash. Had my leave been differently organised I might have been on that very plane.

At the height of the outbreak of hepatitis, during which I saw at least one new case on every morning's sick parade, I found that I could diagnose the condition without even looking at the patient. Keeping my eyes on the desk as each soldier entered the room, if an initial enquiry elicited the fact that the soldier felt generally unwell I would ask them if they were smokers. When a reply came back indicating that the taste of a cigarette had become quite intolerable, the diagnosis of hepatitis was almost certain. Looking up then, the yellow eyes and other classical signs could be easily confirmed.

This epidemic gave me the chance to explore the ruins of the Roman city of Leptis Magna. My classmate Hugh Dinwoodie, who was serving as the medical officer to a small regular army unit located just to the east of Leptis, went down with jaundice. I was sent as his very willing locum for three weeks. Two sights from that brief posting stick in my memory: the often juvenile behaviour of the otherwise very companionable young officers of "J" Battery, 3rd Royal Horse Artillery, playing the apparently traditional after-dinner game of "billiard fives" in their formal dress uniforms; and joining those same officers on the sands to witness the progress of a plague of locusts. We had heard of their imminent arrival and saw the darkening sky, hurrying down to the beach as the first cohorts arrived. A myriad of the pests, filling the air and moving relentlessly across the ground. We stood laughing on the sand, trying to dodge their bodies, crunching scores of them underfoot.

But the memory of Leptis overlies all others from those hot and humid days. As my medical duties at Homs were less than arduous I contrived to spend most of my off-duty hours there. The Pyramids might well have been something to remember; the city in the sand afforded the opportunity of a lifetime.

CITY IN THE SAND

*Great cities decline, they gradually submit to history,
caught in the organic grip of nature and left haunted,
or cruelly stripped of embellishments by man's urge to
plunder. Some vanish; of those which remain, the ruins are
often more majestic and, paradoxically, more human.*
Roloff Beny

The first walk which I took through the ruins of Leptis Magna remains as one of the unforgettable experiences of my life. A few kilometres beyond the town of Homs a path and a few steps led directly downhill from the coastal road to the Severan Arch and the time-worn main street of the ancient city, setting the stage for a figurative descent into the past. The feeling of history became almost overwhelming at the new level, with the silence, the sand and the complete absence of any sign of civilisation combining to provide an easy passage to an entirely different world. Comparing the site in the early 1970s to the miracles of Pompeii and Herculaneum and to what he described as the somewhat battered ruins of ancient Rome, one author expressed his emotions quite simply:

> *Leptis Magna is perfect. It has splendour; it is as complete as any
> reasonable person could wish for; the restorers have been happily
> hampered by political convulsions and lack of funds; above all, you
> can walk the ruins for days on end, and see nobody... Leptis, now
> the sand is being slowly dug away, remains the most complete city
> which has come down to us from the ancient world.*[26]

The sprawling expansion of the eastern outskirts of Homs has changed the landscape around Leptis in recent times, but no such distraction existed in the 1950s. Come with me now as I retrace my footsteps. I defy you to do so without gaining some respect for the history of this venerable city, which grew and flourished over a period

---

26. Menen, A. *Cities in the Sand.* London, Thames and Hudson, 1972.

of at least a thousand years from the earliest Phoenician trading posts to the raising of the last significant building under the Byzantine Emperor Justinian in the sixth century AD.

With the Severan Arch as a starting point, there was evidence at every turn of the twin elements referred to by the famous photographer Rolof Beny, the majesty of the ruins and their humanity. Nothing could be more human than the Severan Arch, strategically placed at the intersection of the city's two main axial roads. With restoration at an early stage at the time of my visit it was like a large and incomplete jigsaw puzzle, the sculptured images of the family of Septimius Severus, the first African Emperor of Rome, standing out to grab one's imagination. A depiction of the triumphal celebration of the return of a famous native son and his family, one might think. The battered face of Geta, however, gave an unintended and poignant hint of a fratricide still to come.[27] Dysfunctional families existed in Roman times just as they do in our own, for everything changes in history, yet nothing does.

The cobbled street led north eastwards from the Arch to the Chalcidicum and the old Market, and then towards the New Forum and the Severan Basilica. Many might cite the latter as the most majestic of the buildings. Once rising to a height of at least thirty metres, the city's judicial centre formed a vast three-aisled and colonnaded hall. When it was finally completed under the Emperor Caracalla in AD 216, one can imagine the ordinary citizen of Leptis being almost overawed by the coloured marble columns and the pilasters depicting the exploits of Hercules and Dionysius, the patron gods of the Severan family. A climb up the stone stairway of the southern apse[28] gave a striking view, not only of the Basilica as a whole but also of one very poignant and human artefact. Amid the rubble near the northern apse stood a makeshift pulpit, fashioned from fallen capitals, a quite different testament from the sculptured artwork of the pilasters. Four Christian churches were built under Justinian, although evidence of only one remains. Looking at that mute pulpit and the stone-barricaded entrances of the adjacent New Forum, it was not difficult to imagine the isolation and desperation of the last citizens of Leptis as the power of the Byzantine Empire finally crumbled.

I found the New Forum, the social and religious centre of the city, even more impressive than the Basilica. Larger than a football field and with only the long northern wall fully restored at that time, the scattered ruins brought the history of the city further alive. Climbing up the steps of the vanished temple of the Genius of Severus, as once did emperors, senators and ordinary Romans, one looked out

---

27. Following the death of Septimius Severus at York in AD 211 his two sons, Caracalla and Geta, were declared joint Emperors. Caracalla had Geta and other family members murdered before the year was out.

28. That climb is still possible today (Dr Alistair Small, personal communication).

over an astonishing jumble of stones, pillars, partially reconstructed or still prostrate capitals and Medusa heads. The centuries could almost be visualised, with Leptis passing from a glorious heyday towards the breakdown of its very existence.

Such thoughts were left behind in a tour of the remainder of the city. A leisurely stroll first through the old market, with its evidence of the Roman shopkeepers' usage of weights and measures; the recreational area of the city, not so very different really from any modern counterpart; the heated areas and steam rooms of the Hadrianic baths, again not so far short of our own technology; the vault of Great Nymphaeum; the gender-distinct public toilets, equipped at that time with running water; and the silted-up remnants of the ancient harbour on the Mediterranean shore.

But if you go to Leptis Magna today leave the real gem to last. The spectacularly situated theatre looks out towards a vast blue sea. Enter by the passageway towards the front of the stage. Above your head you will note the Latin and Punic inscription which commemorates the founder of the building, a citizen of the city named Anobel Rufus. The wording tells of construction through his private financing, and of the theatre's inauguration in the year of the thirteenth Consulship of the Emperor Caesar Augustus (2 BC). Climb one of the many stairways between the rows of grey limestone seats to the uppermost row. Then walk down again, out onto one of the two platforms once reserved for actors who represented the Roman gods. Below you is the many-pillared backdrop to the stage. Take a seat, finally, and think of the atmosphere, the buzz of conversation. You are seated among the audience awaiting a performance, an ancient comedy perhaps. Note the low semi-circular wall separating off the seating area directly in front of the stage. Not much different from our own era, once again, for this section is reserved for the dignitaries of the day. Through the passage way comes Septimius Severus and his entourage, pausing to read the very same inscription which you might have seen a few moments earlier, then stepping out into the open to acknowledge the applause. The Emperor turns to face the stage, and takes his seat. A hush descends, and the comedy begins…

It had not been at all easy to get to Leptis Magna for many years, let alone to Libya, but with Colonel Gaddafi reaccepted into the international community the barriers have been largely lifted. With the city now designated as a World Heritage site, the authorities can boast of many new amenities – slide shows and other information on the internet to study by, local guides, a museum and probably a gift shop. Once I was desperate to return. Now I am not so sure. I walked the ruins nearly every day for three weeks and hardly saw a soul, as did the early archaeologists and a limited number of tourists. That silent and isolated city in the sand was perhaps more perfect than the one which now seeks to attract a modern generation of visitors.

ESCAPE FROM SUEZ

In the case of No 306 Army Dental Centre, Aldershot, one officer and one dental clerk/assistant will be deleted from the establishment, and one bicycle added to the establishment.
Part II Standing Orders,
School of Infantry, Warminster, August 1956

Replace an officer and a clerk by a bicycle? Logical enough, I suppose, in terms of the Standing Orders which regulated all of service life. To us it seemed hilarious, but then we were only National Servicemen, the School of Infantry's resident dentist and I, looking for any light relief during our final days in the forces. With storm clouds gathering over Suez there seemed a distinct possibility that our demobilisation date could be significantly delayed. Two years and a day would have been too much, though to tell the truth it had been great fun while it lasted.

Although the British Army in the 1950s could not have functioned without National Service physicians, they were looked upon with disdain in some quarters. Perhaps it was our minimal training and instant commissioning, perhaps it was the fact that because of our privileged position we could thumb our noses at authority and get away with it. As a sizeable group at BMH Tripoli we simply practised medicine as best we could, laying down our own set of rules. Back in the south of England for my last two months I found a very different atmosphere in the Officers' Mess at Warminster. Surrounded now by career soldiers, I appreciated all the more a story told by a fellow Glasgow graduate.

Jim Allan need never have been in the Services, but wanted the chance to go abroad. When others might have exaggerated a leg weakened by poliomyelitis, he did his best to disguise it, passing the medical with ease. His first posting in the Middle East came as medical officer to a Guards battalion at Sabratha, one of the three Roman cities of the Emporium which gave rise to the name Tripolitania. There he found himself the only non-regular member of a very traditional Officers' Mess, tolerated but not overwhelmingly accepted by his fellow officers. Most of the latter would have preferred an RAMC regular, or someone on a three-year short-service commission. It took a battalion boxing tournament to change their attitude.

Routine medical examinations had been required for all the contestants in the tournament and Jim did not anticipate a significant amount of additional ringside work – an occasional eyebrow to repair, perhaps, but not much more. With the standard of boxing somewhat higher than he had expected, he sat back to enjoy the evening. His social outing didn't last for long. A well contested lightweight bout ended abruptly as one participant swung a haymaker right, immediately clutching at his arm in distress. As the referee stepped between the two boxers, Jim ducked under the ropes and into the ring, quickly confirming his suspicion that the soldier had dislocated his shoulder.

There are two classical ways to remedy such a situation. Jim chose the quicker and more dramatic method, one recognised since the time of Hippocrates, in full view of the regiment. Lying the boxer down on the canvas, he placed his foot firmly in the axilla, lifted up the arm and pulled hard. Though the clunk was audible only at the ringside, the behaviour of the patient was obvious to all, for he stood up immediately, grinning broadly, motioning with his arms as if to continue the bout. Jim helped to usher him out of the ring, thinking that the accompanying applause was for his patient.

As it continued, however, he realised that the instant cure had made him the hero of the hour. His status in the battalion changed dramatically. Subalterns and majors alike, who to that point had almost shunned him, offered their hands and bought him drinks in the Mess, while the rank and file treated him with more deference than their commanding officer. It was a good example of the well-known fact that a physician may often get the most thanks from the simplest of services – with little appreciation sometimes after hours of dedication and stress. Jim wore his halo happily and almost regretted the battalion's return to the UK a few months later. It must have been something of a letdown when he had to join the rest of us in our less than regular mess at the British Military Hospital.

Tripoli was to have a pivotal effect on Jim Allan's whole life. After demobilisation he returned to the city on a contract position as physician to an oil company. He met and courted a young American secretary there and later settled down with her to a lifetime of family practice in Wales. When I visited the old farmhouse he and Kathy had lovingly restored in Newtown, Montgomeryshire, we met at a nearby railway station. After thirty years of contact only by correspondence, he was somewhat larger and I was grey and bald. We walked straight past each other, both later suggesting that the other had changed the more!

As "demob" day approached in that late summer filled by the rhetoric of Eden and Nasser,[29] the dentist and I became increasingly anxious. I wish I could have lightened his days with a final story of those National Service years, but as I was soon to be en route to Kenya I didn't hear its details for more than a year. John Styles had been one of the boys of old Hairmyres, and after a short holiday together in Dublin we shared the square-bashing days at Crookham. While I headed towards Alexandria and the Canal Zone John was on another ship on a much longer voyage to the Far East. Largely ignored by the regular officers in a regimental mess north of Seoul, he took to visiting his medical colleagues at a nearby Australian field ambulance when feeling the need of a quiet drink and a chat, imbibing on his "home" turf only on the rarest of occasions. Twenty months or so later, during the evening of the regiment's penultimate day in Korea, he was approached by the Adjutant of his unit:

'Some ruddy Scotsman you are, Doc. I've never seen you with a glass of whisky at your lips.'

'Maybe not,' replied John, 'but I'll see you under the table any time!'

As time was clearly running short, the challenge was on. Four or five hours and a lot of Scotch later they had almost become friends. Their carousing ended when the Adjutant developed rubber legs and had to be carted off to his camp bed. John managed to make it to his tent on his own steam, though only just. Emerging at six the next morning with a monstrous headache, he was eyed by his batman.

'You look as though you need the hair of the dog who bit you, sir. Let me get you a nice cool beer.'

The Adjutant surfaced, looking considerably the worse for wear. As he tried to adjust his head and eyes to the sunlight he was greeted by the sight of a young medical officer quietly sipping beer. The thought that his rival might have been so occupied all night caused him to groan audibly and then disappear rapidly in the direction of the nearest latrine.

The vanguard of the battalion moved down to the port of Pusan later that same day. As medical officer John had to go with them to present inoculation and health records for travel clearance. This formality concluded, he boarded the troopship for a look around, soon finding himself warmly greeted by the same three nursing sisters with whom he had sailed out to the Far East. The occasion clearly called for a drink. And that is where the Adjutant next saw his tormentor, in the lounge in the officers' quarters on board the ship, still drinking. Apparently he had never stopped! Turning pale once more and muttering something under his breath about bloody Scotsmen, he beat a hasty retreat. Quietly savouring his whisky, John decided that life in the Army might not be so terrible after all. An entirely fitting conclusion to a National Service career.

---

29. British Prime Minister Anthony Eden, President Gamal Abdel Nasser of Egypt.

The great day finally arrived towards the end of August 1956. It was touch and go as to whether our particular intake group would be released, as the crisis caused by Nasser's seizure of the Suez Canal had turned into a major international incident. In the end only those who had opted for three-year commissions were held back. We took a train to London, then seemingly journeyed almost further in an ancient iron-gated lift, down and down to a chamber of underground corridors and window-less office spaces. Uniforms were exchanged for some civilian items, the necessary papers signed, our freedom assured. I bumped into Hugh Dinwoodie in those corridors, the classmate whose illness had led me to Leptis Magna. Well tanned from months in the Libyan sun, Hugh's grin was as wide as my own.

Within ten days I was on my way to a position as an assistant in general practice in Kenya. Although somewhat concerned over my comparative inexperience, particularly in anaesthesia, the opening in the very town where my mother and brother lived seemed too good to pass up. Advance parties of British and French paratroopers were already airborne by the time my South African Airways plane left for Rome and Nairobi, perhaps by an adjusted route. I reckoned I had had a lucky escape from involvement in the ill-fated Suez campaign.

TRAVEL AND TRAINING
THE WHITE HIGHLANDS

Isiolo and Naivasha, Timboroa, Kiambu,
Names like prayers to heaven stealing,
Full of lovely sound and feeling,
Falling on the heart like dew.
from *Poems of Kenya* by Phyllis Haynes

Although almost as spectacular the second time around, the arrival by a first time visitor at the escarpment of the Great Rift Valley in the mid 1950s could only be described in terms of wonder. Little hint came from my brother and mother in the car beside me as we travelled north-west out of Nairobi. Every sight was new for me – the red earth, the Kikuyu women trudging slowly along by the side of the road, bent almost double by the loads on their backs, their unencumbered husbands following some distance to the rear, many pushing bicycles nonchalantly along as if they hadn't a care in the world. Then suddenly one could see forever, with Longonot's sharp peak standing out starkly in a vista that appeared to have no end. I specify the 1950s, for the hundred-mile stretch from Nairobi to Nakuru was at that time the only major Kenyan road covered by tarmac, with long distance haulage the exclusive domain of East African Railways. The coming of the transcontinental lorry traffic dramatically changed that picture. Clear air has now given way to a lingering haze of pollution and the crowded roads provide a constant distraction from opportunities for silent contemplation. For every visitor, however, a stop at the new escarpment is still mandatory before the descent to the floor of the Rift and the journey towards the three soda lakes which run northwards across its basin, Lakes Naivasha, Elementeita and Nakuru.

As the junior assistant in a four-man family practice this was my first foray into private medicine. The location and surroundings of Nakuru, the central town of the so-called White Highlands of Kenya, could hardly have been bettered, and it became a very exciting time in my professional life. Lacking postgraduate hospital experience in anaesthesia and obstetrics, however, I really wasn't properly prepared for such a broad type of general practice, realising almost from the start that I would need to return to the UK to upgrade my practical skills in those two specialities – for my own peace of mind as well as for the benefit of future patients. An important lesson came in the early weeks. 'Just a whiff of ethyl chloride' would be needed, I was told, for the incision of an abscess in a six-month-old infant. I had no experience of using this agent by open mask and judging by the astonishing respiratory and heart rates which the child developed I must have come close to causing a cardiac arrest. The surgeon, Johnnie Johnston, looked even more worried than I felt. "Minor surgery" may be an acceptable term but there is no such thing as a minor anaesthetic. As I was to discover later the first documented death under chloroform occurred prior to a proposed removal of an ingrowing toenail. I had self-made problems on another occasion in Nakuru, too, when using a small dose of a muscle relaxant drug for the very first time, but with much sound advice from Alfred Craddock, one of the other senior partners, I got through the time without any major disaster and the year proved of extraordinary value.

Forced into decisions at a ridiculously early stage in their undergraduate life, today's young physicians miss out on so much, with the pressures of modern medicine giving them only limited opportunities to widen their professional horizons. How on earth can an informed decision on a choice of speciality be taken half-way through medical school, as is currently the case in Canada, at a time when each new rotation presents its own individual appeal? While some may have a clear goal in mind, without a year at least of family practice, without a few more years of life itself in fact, others may make the wrong choice and a number never find the role in life to which they are uniquely suited.

Even apart from a first exposure to a range of parasitic and other tropical diseases, this period in Africa brought me face to face with all sorts of unexpected challenges, some associated with the lifestyles of the developing world. As examples, let me tell you about one problem I faced within a short time of my arrival in Nakuru and then about an evening of obstetrics.

A tall African in his mid-thirties brought his four-year-old son into my surgery. The concern on his face was obvious, as was the extreme pallor of the young boy. 'Can you help my son, Bwana?' he said, in pretty fair English, which was just as well since my Swahili had as yet had little chance to develop. The family history was tragic. Four healthy girls, interspersed by three boys, all of whom had died too young. This fourth son was the father's pride and joy, and now he, too, was ailing in similar fashion to his brothers. There had already been consultations with the doctors at the local African hospital and also earlier at Makerere University in Kampala. Each resulted in the same grim prognosis. As a physician newly arrived in the town, perhaps I might have heard of more recent advances. Could I not help? Surely I could help the *toto*? 'You must do something for my son,' he implored me.

I gained some time with the couple of days necessary for the appropriate diagnostic laboratory tests, but in East Africa in the 1950s it was a losing battle. The sickle cell disease process was too far advanced. The child was going to die, and in the not too distant future at that. Medical school does not teach one how to cope with such a problem, how to make a loving parent with a limited education understand and accept the consequences of a serious hereditary disease, let alone the lack of resources of his country. Why had his daughters thrived and his sons died? 'Shauri ya Mungu' (Swahili for 'the will of God') was about as far as I could get. More than fifty years later, I can still clearly visualise the faces of father and son. I did not sleep well for a good few nights.

Geoff Bird, the assistant in the Nakuru practice whom I was replacing while he went back to the UK to complete his training in obstetrics and gynaecology, phoned me up a few days before his departure:

'Everything seems pretty quiet tonight. Would you like to join me in the labour ward at the Government [African] Hospital? Just to see what's cooking. An evening there can often be pretty interesting.'

"Pretty interesting" turned out to be something of an understatement. Within a matter of four hours, I had performed my first forceps delivery in a reasonably normal case, assisted Geoff in the operating room in dealing with an African lady with a complete rupture of the uterus and then under his expert guiding hands performed a destructive craniotomy on a dead infant, the consequence of another long and obstructed labour in the bush.

Geoff Bird, known as Dicky from his student days in London, was one of the most conscientious and dedicated physicians I have known. Nothing ever seemed too much trouble, no demand from a patient could ever be ignored and financial return was never a significant issue. We shared consulting rooms during my second spell in Kenya and although a minor disagreement eventually forced me into moving out into my own office space, I learned much from him. Around that same time we ran into something of a nightmare at the small Asian Hospital in Nakuru. The acute abdominal pain of a six-year old Ismaili girl had been badly neglected. Extremely ill by the time the local doctor decided to consult Geoff, she had developed generalised peritonitis from an already ruptured appendix. After inducing anaesthesia in the presence of what seemed to be the child's entire family, who resolutely refused to leave the small side-room, we moved her out of their view into the operating room. Shortly after opening the abdomen the theatre lights went out. The back-up generating system then refused to function, leaving us completely in the dark. For thirty minutes we were forced to function with two very basic sources of light. Geoff carried on the surgery with the beam of a small pen-torch, whilst I gleaned what I could of the child's appearance with help of the tiny bulb of my laryngoscope. Not an enjoyable experience, particularly as her colour had been awful to begin with. With no monitors or oximeters in those days, this could best be classed as surgery and anaesthesia by the seat of one's pants. The emotions of the nearby family may well be imagined. Perhaps their prayers assisted towards the eventual successful outcome.

One other memory of Geoff deserves a mention, an occasion between four and five o'clock in the morning when he forced me to drive him twenty miles to view the massed flamingos at dawn on the waters of Lake Elementeita. Although normally eschewing alcohol, he had consumed a fair amount at his farewell party. By the time we reached the Lake he was fast asleep and could not be roused. I parked the car, shivering in the early morning air, for it can be really cool in the Kenyan Highlands at that time of the day, and stomping around for nearly an hour until the early daylight. It proved worth the wait – the complete silence of the lake, the rising sun and the gradual emergence of the wonderfully shaped thorn trees from the surrounding darkness. I never did see even one flamingo. Neither did my companion. He remained more or less oblivious to everything until we got back to Nakuru. On the way I had a glimpse of a pair of giraffes, poetry in motion as they moved effortlessly along a short distance off the road, surely the most graceful of all animals at speed. Africa got into my blood that morning, along with the magic of those Kenyan names. In some measure both are still there.

I shivered even more on another occasion at the most unlikeliest of spots, at the beginning of a motoring holiday with my brother Graham to the Queen Elizabeth Game Park in Uganda. Driving north-west from Nakuru the road climbs steadily towards Mau Summit. By the time one nears Timboroa the altitude is over nine thousand feet. A map of Africa at the side of the road, and a line, proclaims the location – *You are now standing on the Equator*. We had left Nakuru early in the morning, ostensibly because of the long drive ahead, but I suspect also by design on Graham's part, wanting to see my reaction to feeling totally perished on a first crossing of the equator. One highlight of that trip was the astonishing contrast of scenery, for into Uganda and west of Kampala the tropical jungle often encroached on the road, something one never saw in Kenya. We left the dense bush far behind before reaching our ultimate goal at Kazinga, on the border of what was then the Belgian Congo. The clear sight of the Ruwenzori mountains brought lots of adolescent stories and books to mind. Didn't Rider Haggard set his *King Solomon's Mines* in such country?

The long-time game warden of the Queen Elizabeth Park, George Poppleton, was the brother of a good Nakuru friend and we were well looked after. Over the next few days he directed us towards the best viewing spots for the herds of elephants and wallowing hippos to which the Park owed its fame. I got a splendid picture of one of the former of which I am still quite proud, taken without the aid of a telephoto lens. The old bull was very angry, flapping his ears back and forth, debating whether to charge, with Graham ready at the accelerator of his Volkswagen Beetle for a possible rapid retreat. George and his glamorous young European wife, or so she seemed to us bachelors, treated us to a splendid meal the evening before we left. I can almost remember the sounds of that moonlit African night.

Our Ugandan safari was the only holiday I took during that year. One other was planned, but then cancelled for compelling medical reasons. Eight of us, under the leadership of one of the local Nakuru surgeons, Declan O'Keefe, had somewhat optimistically decided to attempt an ascent of Mount Kilimanjaro. We went into training, took up squash and other active pursuits and gave up smoking. I am certain I would have chickened out long before the summit, from a fear of heights rather than the common altitude sickness. Events spared me such ignominy. The second polio epidemic of the 1950s reached our area just one week before we were due to leave, the very first European case in Nakuru being the young four-year-old daughter of our expedition leader. Strenuous exercise is recognised as a dangerous activity for anyone who may be incubating polio, so as close contacts we abandoned our plans. That summit would have been over 19,000 feet. A number of years later I was part of another mixed party who set out to gain the less challenging Mount Elgon in the north-west of Kenya, a mere 14,000. Elgon is more of a walk than a climb, however, and one can drive a car to well over 10,000 feet. Despite that fact, although three of the group made it to the top, I did not. I would never have coped with the snows of Kilimanjaro!

Other memories of 1956 and 1957 stand out: the blue hills of the Subukia Valley where our good friends Billy and Nester Lambert farmed and entertained so successfully and well; a rare view of Mount Kenya from a distance of almost a hundred miles, free that morning from its almost constant small cover of cloud, its pointed peak visible across half the Rift Valley; and two memorable golfing days.

The first of these came in a club match in tea country at the Kericho Club, a one-in-a-million "rub of the green" by any standard. One down with two to play in the four-ball, I had driven into the very tough Kikuyu grass and been forced to pick up. With the opposition both safely on the putting surface Graham then hooked his second shot wildly into even deeper rough. The match was lost, or so it seemed. But no sooner had his ball disappeared from sight than it shot back up into the air again, almost at right-angles, fifty yards and more, ending an astonishing flight mere inches from the pin. We looked at each other in amazement. A small African boy, no more than five or six years old, then rose slowly from the grass, furiously rubbing his head, his siesta rudely interrupted. After missing both of their own birdie attempts the opposition conceded the hole. Still in shock they lost the last to give us the match!

The following morning three of us drove further west and south to the Nyanza Golf Club at Kisumu, on the shores of Lake Victoria. A threesome this time, and no match at stake, but a few hours during which we verified the need for this unique local rule:

> *If a ball lies in dangerous proximity to a crocodile or hippopotamus,*
> *another ball may be dropped, at a safe distance, without penalty.*

That year soon sped by and I returned to Britain as planned, albeit with some regret, disgracing myself in my mother's eyes in the process. Although hard to imagine now the journey from Nairobi to London included two overnight stops, one somewhere in the Sudan and the other on the island of Malta. By the time I reached Heathrow I was extremely hot and tired. With both of my hands full I had stuck my white golfing hat on the back of my head, and my bright pink golfing shirt couldn't have helped. The customs man looked extremely suspicious. He made an exhaustive search of my luggage, emptying every single item onto the bench. At the bottom of the second case he came across a stethoscope. 'Are you a doctor?' he asked, his voice expressing total disbelief. After a half-hearted attempt to stuff my clothes back, he gave up. The interiors of the cases then seemed to have shrunk and with little inclination to repack properly I was left with several loose items. Returning the hat to its perch, I threw my camera strap over my neck, stuffed the extras under both armpits, grabbed my two bags and headed for the exit.

My mother was standing in the front of the waiting crowd, dressed in her Sunday best and with an immaculately clad new friend by her side, brought along to meet her young doctor son. Even more disgusted than the customs officer, she had barely forgiven me by the time I left for Dublin a few weeks later!

MASTERS OF THEIR CRAFT

Experience is the name everyone gives to their mistakes.
Oscar Wilde

S putnik One soared into space on October 4th 1957, bringing a new dimension to a territory previously regarded as the exclusive domain of astronomers, or perhaps of Jules Verne. Readily visible as it tracked across the night sky over Dublin, that first man-made satellite marked a time from which the world was never to be quite the same again. My own circumstances also underwent something of a change of orbit during the four months from September to December 1957 and the period stands out as one of the happiest of my life. Most notable among the number of things which happened was my meeting with a young Irish nurse, of which more later. Other revelations included the taste of draft Guinness and the discovery that this elixir had the capacity to turn non-appetising hospital food into something resembling gourmet fare. Several lifelong friendships date from this time, especially with Gerry Edwards and Norman Coulter-Smith, and I had the privilege of coming in contact with three unforgettable individuals, each a master of a very different craft.

Early that September a small group of postgraduate students gathered together in the operating room of the Rotunda Hospital, myself among them. Our teacher was Dr Andrew ("Drew") Davidson, a master of his craft of obstetrics and gynaecology. A master not only in the sense of a vast experience of the speciality, but also in name, for he had served the seven-year term as Master of the hospital from 1933 to 1940, that title and term having been traditional since the granting of the original Royal Charter by George II in 1756.[30]

There were a dozen or so of us, a pretty motley crowd, with scattered origins in Ireland, Australia, Canada, Scotland and Africa, each at a different point in our professional lives but together now embarked on a month's refresher course at the internationally renowned maternity hospital. By the end of the first week I had already made one firm friend, a general practitioner called Barry Collins from Cork,

---

30. A. Browne ed. *Masters, Midwives and Ladies-in-Waiting*. Dublin, Farmer, 1995.

and one bête noire, an Australian whose long nose seemed to obstruct our view of every case and who seemed to use every possible moment to show off his apparently superior medical knowledge.

The first patient for the day was scheduled for a vaginal examination and possible artificial rupture of the membranes. We could see two anaesthetists making somewhat desultory preparations in the background as the nurses brought the patient into the room and helped position her on the operating table. Now in the thirty-eighth week of her pregnancy, she had suffered an unexpected and minor haemorrhage earlier that morning, an "accidental haemorrhage" in obstetric parlance. Drew outlined the differential diagnosis. Evidence of a mild toxaemia of pregnancy suggested a partial separation of the placenta as the most probable cause, with the never-to-be-forgotten alternative of placenta praevia a possible, but less likely, alternative. He pursued this latter topic, nevertheless, as he donned his gloves, turning first towards our group in the tiered viewing area, emphasising the well recognised dangers of that particular condition, then reassuring and explaining things for the patient. Shortly after beginning his vaginal examination he suddenly stiffened:

'Good God, this feels like a complete placenta praevia… but it can't be, surely, thirty eight weeks and no previous bleeding. I must be feeling blood clot. Just a moment….'

Those were the last words he spoke for around thirty minutes, to us at any rate, for the patient began to bleed. Like an oil well, that is. I had never seen a vaginal haemorrhage of such magnitude, the blood spurting onto the floor in pulsating jets as the anaesthetists frantically tried to start an intravenous infusion, the one essential lifeline they had neglected. We held our collective breaths, watching as the staff quickly prepared for an immediate Caesarean section. The patient turned pale and then a deathly white, her blood pressure dropping disastrously. Somehow, and it could only have been at the last possible moment and due to little else but the grace of God, the junior of the two anaesthetists managed to insert a needle into an ante-cubital vein, allowing them to begin to regain some measure of control of the situation. I don't imagine the lady required much in the way of anaesthesia, for she was in profound shock. After many bottles of intravenous fluid and blood, all administered via needles and from glass bottles, there being no plastic cannulae or bags in those days, she made her way back from the brink of death.

As the very limp baby also began to revive and then to squawk its head off, Drew stripped off his gloves. Leaving his assistants to complete the procedure, he turned towards us:

'Gentlemen… after witnessing such a debacle, if any of you ever examines an ante-partum haemorrhage… in any situation… without having facilities for an immediate Caesarean section and without having an adequate intravenous line, you should be struck off the Medical Register forthwith.'

And with that he walked out the door. Even our Aussie was temporarily lost for words. I felt surprised that he didn't quote Oscar Wilde's definition of "experience"!

I met two other remarkable individuals during those four marvellous months in Dublin, masters of very different crafts. At the end of the postgraduate course a very junior and largely menial position as one of two hospital interns unexpectedly became vacant and I was offered the three-month position. With much time to fill before an upcoming obstetric job in Scotland in the New Year, I jumped at the chance, even for the status commonly referred to by the maternity patients as "the blood pressure doctor". Attendance at antenatal clinics was part of the job, with all the senior obstetricians taking their turns of duty. As he began his examination of the last patient at the end of one morning session in which my own role had largely been that of an observer, Drew Davidson turned to me unexpectedly:

'You play golf, don't you, Humble? I've been let down by a friend. We had a foursome arranged for this afternoon at Portmarnock but now there's only going to be three of us. Would you like to come?'

Would I? I needed little encouragement for a chance to play on the renowned links, and soon headed my Morris Minor along the coast road, finding on arrival that a second member of the group had also called off. Drew disappeared for a moment into the Professional's shop, then casually mentioned on the way towards the first tee that he had arranged for a fourth player. Some fourth player! I recognised the familiar tweed-capped figure at once, the Head Professional at Portmarnock, Harry Bradshaw. With his trademark haymaker swing, Harry was still in his prime at that time, a Ryder Cup player and winner of the individual title at the Canada Cup, the man who had lost a British Open Championship by a single stroke by virtue of having to expend a shot in his second round at Royal St George's when his ball landed inside a broken beer bottle. As the final member of our four-ball turned out to be a near scratch player, it was not the sort of golfing company I was used to, although Drew and I had similar mid-range handicaps. A toss-up decided that I was to be Harry's partner. Significant wagers were set, without any reference to me, and my knees began to knock.

Totally overawed by the enormity of partnering a golfing legend, my initial efforts proved abysmal. But Harry started to talk quietly, telling stories, settling me down by emphasising how much he was going to enjoy taking money from our opponents. Before long he had me playing reasonable golf, by my standards at least, and with his expertise and local knowledge there was little possibility of defeat. I even managed to contribute one hole to our partnership, a birdie two into the stiff wind at the short fifteenth after Harry had shrewdly altered my initial club selection.

What with the wonderful Portmarnock course, the privilege of such a partner for an afternoon, not to mention a significantly replenished wallet, I finished the day in seventh heaven, the pinnacle of my golfing life. Not many ordinary golfers are given the chance of playing with a true master of the game.

A master of obstetrics… a master of golf… what of the third master? In chronological terms he was actually the first of the three, for he had made his presence known to me on my second day in Dublin. But while the other two masters soon passed out of my life, Kevin Liston never totally left it.

I had just arrived in the city. In my belongings somewhere was the name and telephone number of the elder brother of my friend Bill Liston from army days in Tripoli. 'Give him a call when you have settled in,' Bill had told me. 'He and Peggy live in Donnybrook.' That name meant something, so I consulted a dictionary. I hoped it had quietened down a bit since the days of the free fights at its annual fairs! Consulting my road map next, I found that it was somewhere on the periphery of Dublin. Taking a conservative Scots approach to a family I did not yet know, I decided to give myself a chance to find my way around the city first, then perhaps to make contact during the latter part of the first week. I soon discovered that things weren't done that way in Ireland. 'Why have you not called?' Kevin demanded, having placed a phone call to the hospital within twenty-four hours of my landing from the Stranraer-Larne ferry. 'We've been waiting to hear from you.'

As I look back now after Kevin's death, at a friendship that lasted close to forty years, many things have changed. Along with Nelson's Pillar, that Dublin, even that Ireland, has gone. Although not always apparent to the visitor, particularly in the bustle of O'Connell Street, the country's economic outlook was bleak in the 1950s, with emigration near an all-time high. When Ireland moved into its boom years in the 1990s, bursting almost at the seams, with many extended benefits from years of membership in the European Community, numerous celebrities made full use of favourable tax concessions – even stallions came in for very different treatment compared to Britain, their contributions to the Irish economy fully recognised, their unions always with the best of the available mares.[31] Kevin must have been pleased by that, for like all the Irish he loved his racing.

But Kevin Liston also loved his profession. Known and widely respected as the Father of the Irish Bar and as such the individual to whom all his colleagues turned for advice, his talents and personality traits were almost contradictory. Yet there were no contradictions in Kevin Liston's approach to his cases, or to his life, simply an integrity of purpose. Described as a man of stunning modesty and as a barrister who could win a bad case before a good judge, he could be devastating in court whilst remaining entirely polite in manner. I never saw him in this role, of course,

---

31. The recession of 2008-2009 saw the Irish economic tide turn once again.

but I have no difficulty in imagining how he came to be regarded as the most feared cross-examiner that the Irish Bar had produced in half a century. He had a habit of starting most conversations with a slightly hesitant 'Er, yes…' Countless witnesses must have been totally disarmed by this modest beginning, and then pounced upon. He was not to be taken lightly, either, as an opponent at the bridge table or on a golf course. I once saw him hole a full five iron for an eagle two at Milltown Golf Course and react to the occurrence as if it was somehow undeserved.

During the last four months of 1957 I spent many happy hours at Glaunsharoon, the Liston family home. Kevin took me to Lansdowne Road to watch rugby and to Leopardstown for a Saturday at the races. The actor Noel Purcell was in the crowd that day, unmistakable with his fine beard. We played bridge on many winter evenings, and in between times I presumably did enough work to justify the very modest salary offered by the Rotunda. The period culminated in a quite memorable off-duty Christmas day. After a morning begun with Gaelic coffee on the hospital wards, our loss of inhibition led to much hilarity among the mothers on the post-natal ward. Santa Gerry Edwards distributed presents to all the patients at the same time as Norman Smith and I purported to be listening to their foetal hearts! I should emphasise that there was a full quota of physicians on call for the day, their sobriety balancing our lack of such. The shenanigans in the wards completed, we sat down to a lunchtime Christmas meal in the Rotunda dining room and I later rounded off the day in style along with the entire Liston family over a second full spread, one of the happiest family celebrations I can ever remember. It was truly a wonderful time, although with moves afoot which would lead in time to the loss of my bachelor status, I may have had other stars in my eyes. But that is another story.

One final memory of Kevin is worth recording. Though he became godfather to our second daughter our contacts in later years were mostly made by courtesy of the post office. We shared a passion for rugby and corresponded annually around the time of the Ireland-Scotland match. Although fortunes varied from season to season, I always complained at Scotland's lack of the ultimate success, as they had last won the laurels of the Triple Crown in 1938. 'One of these days,' I kept assuring Kevin. Finally it happened, in 1984, after forty-six barren years. And in Dublin, too, when the Scots followed up earlier successes over England and Wales with a 32-9 victory at Lansdowne Road. He loved the telegram I sent him from Canada, a much slower but perhaps more satisfying mode of communication than the modern email. It consisted of just one word – "Hallelujah!"

An enormously hard worker, going to midnight many nights a week, Kevin kept remarkably fit by walking and swimming regularly, working on in his legal rooms until just the week before his death at the age of eighty-eight, and often complaining light-heartedly to his friends that he didn't seem to be getting quite as many legal briefs as he used to.

His eventual passing from this life was wholly in keeping with his deep Christian faith. Vaguely unwell for a couple of days, Kevin had retired to bed early on a Friday evening, complaining of some abdominal pain. Not much better the next day, he nevertheless managed to come downstairs to watch a game of international rugby on the television. His condition worsened during the evening and a consultant came to the house at the request of his son Denis, himself a physician. The likely diagnosis of a massive mesenteric thrombosis having been confirmed, a decision was taken to do nothing more than to keep him as comfortable and pain-free as possible. He died quietly at home during the Sunday. Kevin Liston had been called to the Irish Bar in 1928. In the long career that followed he more than earned the title of master of his craft.

IN AT THE DEEP END

Caesar said to me, 'Dar'st thou, Cassius, now,
Leap with me into this angry flood,
And swim to yonder point?' Upon my word,
Accoutrèd as I was, I plungèd in,
And bade him follow...
But ere we could arrive the point propos'd,
Caesar cried, 'Help me Cassius, or I sink!'
Shakespeare

I t seems almost incomprehensible that training in one of the specialities of medicine could follow such a course. After ten months of obstetrics I had embarked on the second of my postgraduate objectives, the gaining of experience in anaesthesia, arriving at the four-hundred-bed hospital in Paisley in the West of Scotland on a Wednesday morning. After spending the next two days not doing much more than chatting in the operating room with the Head of the Anaesthetic Department, Dr Joe Hill, I was somewhat taken aback when he casually remarked that he was off to his Loch Long cottage for the weekend:

'You seem to know what you are doing, Humble. Will you look after the emergencies? Phone me if there are any problems.'

So there I was, with no anaesthetic training of any consequence and only a handful of cases under my belt, thrown in at the deep end to sink or swim. Caesar at least had Cassius for company! An inexperienced and single-handed anaesthetist has far more worries, the survival of each unsuspecting patient coming first to mind. The astonishing thing is that the system worked – after a fashion at least – and that many of us in that era learned the rudiments of airway management this hard way, getting ourselves in and out of trouble without the assistance trainees have today. An acute appendix and a couple of fractured wrists were the only emergencies that first weekend. All survived, fortuitously or otherwise, and my anaesthetic career was underway.

Muscle relaxant drugs were quite new to me, but Joe only used small doses, with assisted rather than controlled ventilation the order of the day. We had no recovery rooms, no ventilators, no anaesthetic records and no monitors of any kind, although we followed pulse rates and blood pressures closely with our fingers and ears. Ether and trilene were the main volatile anaesthetics, cardiac irregularities being very frequent when using the latter of these two agents. Although he had no idea of the exact nature and significance of these arrhythmias, Joe's commonsense methods kept him out of trouble, not pushing the trilene, reducing its concentration when problems arose, giving a very small dose of an intravenous narcotic to allow this reduction, and quietly assisting the ventilation. We did not take the advice of a prominent American anesthesiologist who claimed much success from taking a walk twice round the operating room whenever a patient's pulse developed a significant irregularity under cyclopropane anaesthesia! Except for major surgery or where a blood transfusion might be anticipated, intravenous fluids were seldom administered; indeed my boss rarely had an open intravenous line which he could use in any emergency. I remember being complimented by one of the surgeons because of my habit of keeping a syringe strapped to the back of the patient's hand for intermittent drug administration, with the plunger taped to the sides of the barrel to prevent the needle blocking off with blood. Much of the time it worked. Often it did not, and I well recall a sense of wonder and delight on being introduced to indwelling Mitchell and Gordh needles. There were no intravenous catheters in those days and therefore no guaranteed control, but these needles were a considerable step forward.

Joe Hill appeared to know the social history of almost every local family, so patients had usually lost most of their nervousness prior to going off to sleep. Although already falling behind the times in his methods, he did teach me a number of valuable maxims, notable among them the fact that one is more liable to get into trouble if a spontaneously breathing patient is too lightly anaesthetised rather than the reverse, and that while noisy breathing is always obstructed breathing, obstructed breathing is not always noisy. Our monitors were our senses, and while today's generation uses sophisticated equipment to track the depth of anaesthesia, the basic rules have not changed. Since we never intubated patients without a specific indication, laryngeal spasm caused the majority of our difficulties.

One case stands out. A large lady, a bit over five feet and weighing well over three hundred pounds, was scheduled to have a simple five-minute operation performed by the junior gynaecological registrar at a small local hospital. Few veins were evident, but I did manage to find one that lasted long enough for me to give what in retrospect must have been an inadequate amount of pentothal. Any anaesthetist can envisage the downward spiralling course of events: a series of coughs followed by a rapidly progressive and unremitting laryngeal spasm; a completely tight and unyielding reservoir bag, with absolutely no possibility of getting any oxygen into her lungs; a colleague trying desperately to find a vein on my behalf; the patient turning blue, then black, then grey. By the grace of God, however, her larynx relaxed at the very last moment, as did the bag, allowing me to force a few precious breaths of oxygen into the lungs. We abandoned the operation and I nearly gave up anaesthesia on the spot. It was a valuable lesson. Nowadays one would never think of embarking on any anaesthetic without an open intravenous line, let alone in the presence of significant obesity where airway control can so easily be lost. One should make a film of the above sequence, or perhaps one of a smoker coughing his or her lungs out in a recovery room. Anaesthetists and some of their patients might live longer!

Yet if this training in Paisley stemmed mainly from the old art of the speciality as opposed to its more modern science, it had a built-in safety factor, one which may be overlooked today amidst the plethora of newer monitoring devices. Without such assistance the anaesthetist remained at the head of the patient, one hand on the pulse and the other on the reservoir or "re-breathing" bag. Although I hate the North American abbreviation, this practice fits the styling of that old method of anaesthesia as being "high touch, low tech" – close personal contact with a minimum of technical equipment. In the brave new technical world a "high touch" personal element must never be forgotten.

Although this is moving forward in my story for a moment, consider the problem of unrecognised oesophageal intubation.[32] In comparative terms at least, this iatrogenic (i.e. caused unintentionally) disaster reached disturbingly high proportions in North America and Europe in 1980, a low point for our speciality during my years in practice. I can remember there had been three fatalities in Canada, one in Edmonton, one in Vancouver and one in Ontario. I walked into my first session at the World Congress of Anesthesiology in Hamburg that September to hear an American describing a similar incident from his own state and later listened to Professor Cecil Gray of Liverpool detailing a number of other cases reported to the Medical Defence Union. 'What on earth are we doing???' I wrote in my notebook at the time. Discussions on this topic with younger colleagues have not always been productive, for they have not gone as far back in their reading as a textbook of anaesthesia from the 1950s entitled *Anaesthetic Accidents*,[33] which devotes a full chapter to the complications of endotracheal intubation without making any mention of oesophageal intubation, recognised or unrecognised. History is here providing

32. For the benefit of lay readers I should explain that for most major surgery under general anaesthesia the airway is secured by the passage of a tube into the trachea (or windpipe). Done with the aid of a laryngoscope, this procedure may vary from being extremely simple to extraordinarily difficult. In the latter case the tube can enter the oesophagus (or gullet). Failure to detect such misplacement is clearly disastrous.

33. Keating, V. *Anaesthetic Accidents*. Chicago, Year Book Publishers, 1956.

a lesson, as it so often does, that these cases came hand in hand with increasing reliance on mechanical ventilators. We were taught never to hook a patient up to a ventilator until auscultation of the lungs and the feel of the bag confirmed the correct positioning of the endotracheal tube. Although a new type of monitor has now brought an answer to this particular problem,[34] clinical acumen and constant vigilance are still required.

The difficulties of the Paisley job did not always relate to anaesthesia. Classic "pea-soup" fogs were frequent in the area during the winter of 1958-59, with the pollutant haze even entering the corridors of our hospital. The phone in my room rang on one such evening:

'We have a woman who needs a general anaesthetic for a forceps delivery. There is significant foetal distress. Can you come right away?'

The call came from the sister in charge of the labour ward at Thornhill Maternity Hospital, under normal driving conditions some ten to fifteen minutes away. I looked out the window before replying: 'I'll never make it in time; the visibility looks desperate.'

'You'll have to try. Conditions aren't that bad here. We must have you – as soon as you can, please.'

I took a deep breath as I got behind the wheel of my Morris Minor. This was asking a bit much even for that best of all small cars. Almost totally lost within seconds, I contrived to negotiate a major roundabout in completely the wrong direction, the only thing saving me the fact that few other fools had ventured out on such a night. With one hand on the wheel and my eyes glued to the kerb through the passenger-side window, I negotiated the miles a yard or two at a time, quite the worst driving conditions I have ever experienced except for a winter blizzard years later on the Edmonton to Calgary highway in Alberta. Although visibility started to improve nearer Thornhill, by the time I arrived a healthy infant was squawking its head off, successfully delivered by forceps under local anaesthesia. The staff were very apologetic, commiserating over a brief cup of tea before informing me that I was needed back at the Infirmary for another urgent emergency. Back into the fog I went, for such was the lot of a junior anaesthetist!

If that particular evening was a nightmare on the road, I used to endure personal nightmares in one of the Infirmary's operating rooms. Joe Hill and the other consultant did not attend the twice-a-week tonsil and adenoid sessions, so my early instruction and much support came from Dorothy Walby and Audrey Symonds, the other members of the junior staff. After a number of such shared mornings I was left to my own devices, a cross between flying blind and being thrown in at the deep end! A dozen or more young children to be induced each day by ethyl chloride and open

---

34. End-tidal CO2 (carbon dioxide) monitors.

drop ether via an Ogsten mask, a product of the late nineteenth century. The depth of anaesthesia was quite critical, for after the guillotine removal of the tonsils the children had to be quickly turned onto their sides, with the adenoidectomy then performed as they regained consciousness. Too deep and they were unable to cough out blood, too light and they were liable to clamp down fiercely on the adenotome. One only heard the results of this latter battle, as the surgeon always supervised the immediate recovery of each patient, the anaesthetist being required to induce the next child on another operating table a few feet away – to the accompaniment of anything up to full-blooded screams. Porters whisked each successive victim away to a nearby room where they completed their recovery, lying on the floor in a welter of blood, tears and vomit. How many nightmares did these children suffer following such experiences, I wonder? I got over mine eventually, although it took me a number of weeks to gain real confidence in my ability to produce the correct level of anaesthesia.

Di-ethyl ether, to give anaesthetic ether its full name, remains a fascinating drug. Despite its many disadvantages, the smell and irritant nature of the vapour, the long induction and slow recovery and the frequent occurrence of post-operative nausea and vomiting, it possessed one remarkable advantage. A respiratory depressant, like all the volatile anaesthetic agents, it could be given to the point of almost complete cessation of respiratory movement without any significant effect on the heart. When further administration was stopped at this point, with only the diaphragm still working, the intercostal muscles would slowly begin to recover and chest movement recommence. No cardiac irregularities were seen. Once a stormy induction with open drop ether was over, provided the pattern of respiration could be observed, even a totally inexperienced person could be instructed in its subsequent administration. Many a shipboard operation was conducted along such lines, the doctor inducing "rag and bottle" anaesthesia before switching to the surgical task at hand, instructing a sick bay attendant or able-bodied seaman when to administer more or less ether. I feel fortunate in having been able to use ether extensively, even in young infants, along with other agents such as chloroform, ethyl chloride, cyclopropane and trichlorethylene which have long since been retired from service.

Although I did study the books at that time in preparation for diploma examinations in both anaesthesia and obstetrics, thinking back to those days of being thrown in at the deep end I consider myself fortunate to have learned the art of anaesthesia the hard and practical way first, long before receiving proper instruction in its science. The anaesthetist of the early twenty-first century should try to imagine the following scenario: a run down and poorly equipped private nursing home in the 1950s; a purely inhalational anaesthetic to be given by mask for a forceps delivery; the mother, obese and short-necked with an exceedingly difficult airway, turned across a sagging bed with her legs held by two nurses, that activity therefore eliminating them as assistants for any other purpose; and an ancient anaesthetic machine from the 1930s with a suction apparatus requiring activation by foot pump. Plain hard work – Paisley taught me that and more.

Towards the end of the year I started looking for posts as an assistant in mixed general and anaesthetic practice jobs in East or Central Africa, finding one that seemed ideal in Bulawayo, Southern Rhodesia (now Zimbabwe), one of the three members of the new Central African Federation. Despite rumblings of political unrest in the region, after my earlier taste of Africa I didn't really fancy what I saw as the humdrum of the National Health Service. With a new position soon accepted, one daunting prospect remained, a trip to the south-east corner of Ireland to undergo the close scrutiny of my girl-friend Betty's family. Each sign on the road south from Dublin carried two names, Wexford, where I was headed for, and another place called Loch Garman. I couldn't for the life of me find this latter name on my map and kept waiting for a turn off to that loch. If that name had looked the least bit like a Gaelic one, I might have guessed much sooner that it was Irish for Wexford!

I was given a thorough going over after arriving at the small village of Taghmon, initially by the ladies and then by some of their menfolk. The Quigley family turned out to be an extended one. That first evening it seemed to me that as many as fifty female relatives and friends crowded into a house opposite the pub owned by Betty's brother Paddy. Having survived this inspection, more or less, I ran into greater difficulties the following day at an early lunchtime session across the road when the three Quigley brothers set out with malice aforethought to see if this Scotsman could hold his drink. By the time I started my third glass of lager they had each put away four or five pints of Guinness. I might be there still if their sister had not come to my rescue. I suppose I passed muster, but it was a close call! I escaped back onto the Dublin road the following day with something of a hangover, en route for Southern Rhodesia and our wedding in Kenya the following year.

FROM RHODES
TO LIVINGSTONE

The wind of change is blowing through this continent.
Harold MacMillan,
Cape Town, South Africa, February 3rd 1960

There is a scene in Richard Gordon's *Doctor in the House*[35] which may have stretched the credulity of some readers. A medical student taking his final practical exam in Obstetrics is invited by an examiner to demonstrate his proficiency in the application of forceps by applying them to a foetal doll pre-positioned inside a bony female pelvis. He has some difficulty with the application and with the ensuing extraction of the mock foetus. Slipping on the floor, he despatches baby, pelvis and the two separate blades of the instrument over his shoulder with momentum in the general direction of the examiner. The latter grimly surveys the carnage, leans down and picks up one of the blades, remarking as he passes it over: 'Now hit the father over the head and you'll have killed the whole b— family!'

That story made splendid fiction. The following tale, unfortunately, is fact. Neil Ransford had gone to his farm for the weekend and as his new assistant in the Bulawayo practice I was taking calls. A request came for an anaesthetic for a forceps delivery. I don't recall the specific indication for the instrumental delivery but at the outset it did not involve any question of maternal or foetal distress. The attending physician, a general practitioner whom I had not previously met, was washing his hands when I arrived. His voice sounded somewhat strange as he gave me some brief details, but I put this down to the fact that he had already donned a cloth mask. I went ahead and got the patient off to sleep.

Even before the attempted application of the forceps it became obvious that we had a major problem on our hands. Poorly co-ordinated in both thought and action, the doctor was clearly under the influence of alcohol. What on earth was I going to do? Not long arrived in the city, I knew nothing of this individual. The anaesthetic equipment still felt a bit strange, as did the white-habited nuns in the

---

35. Gordon, R. *Doctor in the House.* London, Joseph, 1952.

delivery room. They looked as worried as I felt, but remained silent. After a number of fumbled attempts, some sort of application of the forceps blades was achieved. Inadequately locked together, however, they slipped off the baby's head when he began the surprisingly strong pull that is often required. He staggered and almost fell, clutching one blade as the other clattered onto the floor behind him. I asked if he would like us to get some help, but he angrily refused, asking instead for another sterile pair of forceps. As he began a second attempt at the delivery, I motioned to one of the nuns. At two am, with one and possibly two lives at very considerable risk, there was no time for any niceties as to who was junior or senior: 'Call one of the obstetricians – any of them – and hurry!'

The ensuing ten to fifteen minutes rate among the most anxious and unpleasant of my professional life. With no examiner to dismiss him in the withering terms of Gordon's tale, the impaired doctor continued his futile efforts. If there had been no foetal distress at the start, at this rate it wasn't going to be long in developing. Damage to the baby's head and face seemed inevitable. I again asked if he needed any help. His response did not change. Short of leaving the anaesthetic to one of the nuns and forcibly taking over, which could have had other consequences for the mother, there was little I could do except pray that help would soon arrive. I'm sure the sisters were similarly occupied.

Our saviour walked in at last, taking in the scene at a quick glance. 'I'll do this,' he announced, in a voice that brooked no opposition. White and shaken, the other stood back, swaying occasionally and not uttering a single word for the rest of that night in my presence. Whenever we met during the remainder of my stay in the city he pointedly failed to meet my eyes. I told my boss about the debacle, but whether any restriction of obstetric privileges was ever applied I have no idea. I left that to my superiors. Somehow I doubt it, just as I doubt that the mother ever knew anything of the peril she and her child were in. In those days such things were more likely to be covered up. Despite a number of bruises and abrasions to the face and head, the baby did amazingly well. Gordon Ostlere was a career anaesthetist before he adopted the pen name of Richard Gordon and became a bestselling novelist. I have often wondered if he had witnessed a similar incident. Or was the classic examination scene simply the product of his fertile imagination? Fact can be just as strange as fiction at times – and more dangerous.

Although I received some wonderful hospitality, made a number of good friends and learnt a great deal more about general practice and anaesthesia, I never really settled into life in Rhodesia. Perhaps I should not have ignored the early omens. Neil Ransford's offer of a job arrived in an envelope addressed to Helensburgh, "North Britain". I nearly turned it down flat. The Romans may have thought of the inhabitants of our small country in those terms but surely by the 1950s even an Englishman should have known better! As the position in a mixed general and anaesthetic practice seemed just what I was looking for, I swallowed any built-in prejudices and sent off my acceptance. Just one week later I had even greater cause to question the move, for the Prime Minister of the new Central African Federation, Sir Roy Welensky, announced a state of emergency in the country. But those were the days before Harold Macmillan's famous "wind of change" speech and I decided that perhaps Rhodesia would soon put these troubles in the past, as Kenya had apparently done further to the north. How wrong can one be?

Even the journey had its problems. I flew out via Rome and Athens in a more than half-empty South African Airways plane, stopping in Kenya for a short holiday to visit my mother and brother and renew Nakuru friendships, then on to Salisbury (Harare) aboard a BOAC Britannia. The "whispering giant" they called that plane. A lumbering giant might have been a more appropriate description. Quite apart from losing many hours en route from a combination of mechanical problems and a strong head wind, our particular aircraft seemed to take forever to take off, seemingly utilising every single foot of the runway. At each of the three intermediate stops I felt certain we were about to crash. The connecting flight to Bulawayo missed, I got compensation in the form of a complimentary dinner and overnight stay at Salisbury's famous Meikle's Hotel. The atmosphere in the dining room made me think. Europeans only at the tables; a white orchestra playing palm court music; food and drink in abundance served by innumerable black waiters, green uniformed and wearing red cummerbunds; the very best of colonial living in fact, but in the event a way of life heading slowly towards its end.

Visibility was excellent on the flight early next morning from Salisbury to Bulawayo and we flew at quite a low altitude. I couldn't get over the terrain. I had never seen such flat country. Much of the Canadian prairies now seem hilly by comparison. Not a single bump or blip on the landscape as far as the eye could see, a few scattered farms and small towns, otherwise nothing. After the wonder of the Rift Valley and the beauty of Kenya Highlands, first impressions were not favourable.

'Neil Ransford should have been an Oxford don,' his son Andrew wrote following his father's death in 1989. In spite of an exceedingly busy professional life, initially in the Colonial Medical Service and later in private practice in Bulawayo, my new boss went on to equal the output of many full-time academics, producing no fewer than eight books on diverse aspects of the history and development of south and central Africa. Several of these are rightly regarded as classics. Two remain my special favourites, the second a dramatic and totally fascinating account of one of the major battles in the First Boer War.[36]

---

36. Ransford, O. *Livingstone's Lake – The Drama of Nyasa*. London, John Murray, 1966 and Ransford, O. *The Battle of Majuba Hill*. London, John Murray, 1967.

Neil's practice often took on an almost frantic pace, with house calls done so early that we were frequently greeted by family members in dressing gowns or house coats, sleep still being rubbed from their eyes. At seven-thirty on Sunday mornings he routinely held a mini-clinic at his house for those requiring daily injections of penicillin and the like. I arrived five minutes late to conduct such a session when Neil was supposed to be off-call. He had already dealt with most of the patients. As the last departed I received the full fury of his tongue. If he had an obvious weak spot in his character it showed up in occasional outbursts of temper, almost of uncontrollable rage, as on this occasion. His work ethic and talent were evident in everything he did, however, equally at home in the diverse roles of family physician, anaesthetist, author and historian.

Another local anaesthetist had a very different reputation in the local medical circles, impossible to defend either then or now. Well qualified and extremely capable, he nevertheless made a habit of "supervising" many of his anaesthetics from the coffee room of the operating suite. All but his minor cases were paralysed and placed on a mechanical ventilator, in exemplary fashion it must be stressed. He would then depart to the adjacent room for coffee, glancing in from time to time to confirm that all was well – this in an era possessing none of the luxuries of today such as pulse, heart or oxygen monitors. One morning I was assisting a surgeon in a major operation. Absorbed in a difficult dissection, deep in the abdomen, we called out in alarm as the blood became exceedingly dark. The anaesthetist rushed back, rapidly discovering that an x-ray technician had inadvertently disconnected his ventilator. One minute's hypoxia… two minutes… difficult to tell in retrospect, but in the event no lasting harm to the patient.

Although he continued to get away with his negligent pattern of practice the coffee drinker met his match in the end. The wife of local ENT specialist Bill Taylor was due to have her gall-bladder removed. Knowing of the reputation for wandering, her husband elected to sit himself down in the coffee room for the duration of the surgery. From my vantage point as the surgical assistant in the case the antics during the hour-long procedure became almost comical to watch, each and every attempt at a foray into the coffee room being quickly aborted by a glimpse of Bill's blandly smiling face.

My mornings were split between surgical assisting and anaesthesia. Private and government-run hospitals, nursing homes, medical suites and isolated dental offices, we covered them all, with the physical space, anaesthetic equipment and even the operators at times leaving something to be desired. One day stands out. It began in a small examination room in an office building where a local orthopaedic surgeon used to perform spinal manipulations under anaesthesia, tossing patients alarmingly back and forth across a couch whilst they were briefly rendered unconscious and paralysed. With whispered rumours of past neurological disasters, I always felt extremely uncomfortable doing these cases. Breathing a sigh of relief at the end of this particular session, I moved on to a fourth-floor dental office which was totally isolated from any emergency help, finding there an antiquated McKesson apparatus with which I was barely familiar. I never quite decided who was to blame, the machine or myself, but between us we precipitated a most alarming hypoxic episode in a ten-year-old boy, made worse by the fact that the boy's mother had insisted on remaining in the room. With her white face a stark contrast to the happily restored colour of her son, she must have come very close to passing out. Volunteering to have the machine checked out before further use, the dentist looked none too happy either. I consoled myself by recalling Gordon Ostlere's story of another dental anaesthetic.

Before branching fully into his second life, Ostlere wrote a small textbook on anaesthesia.[37] Covering the basic tenets of the speciality remarkably well, its pages were enlivened by a number of his trademark stories. Illustrating the maxim that an anaesthetist must never lose his head in an emergency, he told of a dental session in London on a very hot summer afternoon. Four people were involved: a young child requiring the extraction of a single tooth, a mother who resolutely refused to leave her son's side, an elderly dentist and an anaesthetist. Immediately following the induction of anaesthesia the dentist collapsed, overcome by the stifling heat. Imagining that he had suffered a heart attack, the mother promptly fainted, thus leaving the anaesthetist with three unconscious patients instead of one. Not a bit deterred, he extracted the offending tooth with the dental forceps, threw the tumbler of mouth wash over the face of the dentist and pressed the cold ether-soaked sponge against the neck of the mother, leaving the trio to sort themselves out as he headed off to his next case. As I headed off to mine, I recalled W. S. Gilbert's line about the lot of a policeman and wondered what he might have written about the lot of the anaesthetist!

Although I have complained about the flatness of the surrounding area, one actually didn't have to travel far from Bulawayo to find a place of rare charm and beauty, the Matopos Hills National Park. Approaching from the south, the visitor arrives at a decorative stone wall and entrance gate. Engraved on a tablet are the following words:

> *This ground is consecrated and forever set apart for those who have deserved well of their country.*

Laudable sentiments, perhaps, were it not for the fact that such memorials have been second-guessed by the march of history. Although the name of Cecil Rhodes

---

37. Ostlere, G. *Anaesthetics for Medical Students*. London, Churchill, 1949.

is not mentioned on the tablet, he chose a nearby site in these lovely surroundings for his final resting place. A simply carved gravestone lies between two enormous boulders, looking out over a wonderful distant vista that must have represented for him the length and breadth of his dream for a Southern Africa united under the British Crown. Not far away stands the huge memorial to the Jameson Raid, the unauthorised attack on the Transvaal which triggered the early events of the Boer War and indirectly led to Rhodes' resignation as Governor of Cape Colony. The peace and beauty of the Matopos Hills are an abiding memory. One wonders how the area is currently promoted by the authorities in Zimbabwe. I imagine that the deeds of Rhodes and Jameson are nowadays more likely to be vilified than glorified.

If neither the city of Bulawayo, nor the country of Rhodesia, appealed enough after six months to deter me from a return to Kenya, there was one other unforgettable highlight, the three-hundred-mile trip to the Victoria Falls along what must surely rank among the straightest stretches of road in the world. Two strips of tarmac on a soft murram base, one of which had to be vacated when any vehicle approached from the opposite direction. With not a bend in the whole journey – well, perhaps one – the "tramlines" stretched as far as the eye could see, holding both mirage-like and hypnotic qualities. With such perfect conditions for fatigue-related accidents, my friend John Kennedy Smith and I were more than happy to stop overnight at the Wankie Game Reserve, renowned for its elephants.

Jake and I saw the Victoria Falls at perhaps their best, not too full and hence not obscured by the spray. 'The smoke that thunders', the Matabele description of the Falls, is a wonderful name, appreciated with anticipation first from the nearby hotel. Nothing disappointed: each successive section of the falls, from west to east; walking down the wooden steps till one stood behind and inside the eastern cataract; watching an orange sun set in the evening; sipping gin and tonic on the Zambezi's edge, contemplating the history of the region in silence – Stanley and Livingstone and the rest; an overview by small plane the following morning, flying low over the great chasm and the tortuous canyons of the Zambezi; and a game-viewing flight over Bechuanaland to top everything off.

Before leaving we photographed each other in front of the nearby statue of Livingstone and drove across the border into Northern Rhodesia (Zambia) to the town which still bears the name of the great Scottish missionary explorer. Even today he is remembered there through a museum and an annual festival.. On the very last page of his seventh book on the history of the region,[38] a work which gives a fine reassessment of the explorer's life, Neil Ransford set down Livingstone's assertion that 'all will come right someday' and concludes with his valedictory message:

---

38. Ransford, O. *David Livingstone – The Dark Interior*. London, John Murray, 1978.

...it is [to be] hoped that on the African continent our deeds may in our children's days bear fruits worthy to be held in everlasting remembrance.

Despite the fact that the history of the colonial exploitation of Africa may be regarded as the very antithesis of those words, the memory of a man whose life was dedicated to the abolition of the slave trade has not been swept away by the wind of change.

At the end of my six-month assistantship, Neil offered me the chance of a junior partnership. There were many strings attached, however, and I had begun to hanker for a return to Kenya, especially after learning of an opportunity to open my own practice in Nakuru. Although a significant challenge in financial terms, the chance to do so might never come again. I toyed with the idea of driving all the way north, but in the end decided to sell my almost new Ford Anglia and risk a flight aboard another Britannia.

DIAGNOSIS AND PROGNOSIS
A QUESTION OF LIFESTYLE

A taste for drink, combined with gout,
Had doubled him up for ever.
from *Iolanthe*, by W. S. Gilbert

The year was now 1961, my shingle duly hung. After a very sparse initial period, waiting and hoping that patients would start to come, the practice had thrived. The township of Nakuru stood on the lower slopes of Menengai, an extinct volcano. European settlers numbered around three thousand, many living on prestigious hillside sites looking southwards towards Lake Nakuru, a popular draw for tourists even then with its massed flocks of flamingos and nowadays the central attraction of an internationally famed National Park. There was also a size-able Asian community, which included most of the town's shopkeepers, and an even larger African population who lived in a scattered shanty town, closer to the soda dust which blew up from the lake in the dry season.

My racially mixed practice still reflected the fading days of colonialism, for before I started my morning's work giving anaesthetics at the eighty-bed European hospital I would come in early to see any African patients in the office I shared with Geoff Bird. For the remainder of the day other races had joint use of a large single waiting room. Our nurse-receptionist Mrs Wilkinson was very house-proud, usually finding an excuse to perform something of a spring-clean after anyone had been in that room whom she judged to be less than desirable. She came to the door of my examining room late one afternoon, extremely flustered, whilst I was talking to the first of three maternity patients. 'Some kind of chief has been brought in,' she whispered, 'and he doesn't have much on in the way of clothes. Can you come out and see him straight away?'

A very large African was seated between the two ladies. His body odour was significant. Apart from several necklaces, his only clothing consisted of a skimpy kilt or skirt. Three henchmen stood behind him, one carrying a cloth bag. Mrs Wilkinson remained agitated, obviously anxious to get him out of her waiting room.

'He can't walk,' she said. 'They carried him in. Can we get him into the treatment room at the back? Quickly!'

The chief must have weighed three hundred and fifty pounds. When the three henchmen lifted him up, the major source of Mrs W.'s agitation became all too evident. With the skirt barely covering his huge waist, and no other clothing underneath, his very considerable masculine charms were alarmingly displayed for all to see. The two ladies bravely looked away. We got him onto the examining table in the back room. Mrs W. mopped her brow.

Since he spoke no English and I had only a few words and phrases of Swahili it proved difficult to get a proper story, but he obviously had a major problem with one knee, which was grossly swollen, hot to the touch and extremely tender. I had never seen an acute gouty arthritis of the knee but this seemed a likely possibility. We reached a consensus on his lifestyle largely by means of gestures; well looked after by his followers in every respect, he drank considerable quantities of cheap red wine.

Under his very curious gaze, I took some blood from a vein in one arm. Since African patients in those days did not think any treatment worthwhile unless it included a "shindanu", or injection, preferably a painful one, I favoured his large backside with a vitamin product, phoning my golfing buddy Austin Riley then at the hospital laboratory to see how long it would take to get the blood checked for its uric acid level. He said I could have the result by the middle of the following morning.

'Bring him back at two pm tomorrow,' I told the henchmen.

Mrs Wilkinson objected vehemently. 'You have patients booked for that time. They will have to bring him in by the back entrance.' She had no intention of allowing a repeat of the same spectacle in her front waiting room! Eventually we settled for twelve-thirty, with both of us foregoing lunch.

To cut a long story short, it was indeed acute gout. I instructed the attendants to bring him back every day, primarily to make sure he was taking the appropriate pills, administering a shindanu each time. The swelling and pain rapidly receded and his mobility steadily improved. On the last visit he walked in unsupported, beaming all over his face, and shook my hand vigorously. 'Asanta sana, Bwana,'[39] he repeated over and over again. Mrs W. still fussed in the background, anxiously watching his every move. After that first day, however, she had successfully organised the times of the chief's appearances to make sure he was never again seen by any of my other patients.

I charged him five shillings per consultation, my usual rate for African patients, one-third of the European rate. Each time he paid in silver from the cloth bag. I tried to impress on him some rudimentary ideas of diet and lifestyle, for he was planning to return up-country and I had no great hopes that he would continue to

---

39. Swahili for 'Thank you very much, master.'

take the prophylactic anti-gout medication which I had prescribed. After giving me the final fee, he asked one of his attendants to hand over the bag. Slowly counting out one hundred single shillings (five pounds), he laid the coins on the table between us. Another handshake and he was gone. I have had many presents from grateful patients but this was the only time in forty years of practice that any of them ever left me a tip!

Although I never saw him again, I did hear about the chief a number of months later. He had been admitted to an up-country hospital after a recurrence of the same problem. Sadly, a doctor there had opened up his knee. After a complicated post-operative course he could no longer walk, having to be constantly carried around by his henchmen. Lifestyles are no respecters of persons.[40]

---

40. I sent this story to the *Weekly Telegraph,* where it was published in August 1998 under the title "Taking tips on a case of gout".

MANY DIFFERENT FACES

Diagnosis is one of the commonest diseases.
Karl Kraus (1874-1936)

It had been a perfect morning when I answered the telephone in my office. On the short drive to the hospital I even found time to notice that the jacaranda trees on the east end of Donald Avenue were at their best, and that the daily clouds had not yet begun to gather. Like a perpetual English summer, but with predictable late afternoon rains; in those years the climate of the Highlands of Kenya could hardly be bettered.

Less than half an hour later I looked down from a second floor window, the tranquillity of the day forgotten. I could see the young army officer pacing up and down on the lawn. No words could soften the news I now had to give him. A scant three weeks after their arrival in the country, his seemingly healthy young wife lay dead in the ward behind me. What burden of guilt might lie on his shoulders, perhaps for the remainder of his life? And as for myself, I was rapidly discovering that malaria had many faces, often very different from the clear-cut pictures presented by the textbooks. While the diagnosis might offer little difficulty in the presence of a typical paroxysmal attack, the reverse applied in some chronic or sub-acute situations. Simply considering its possibility was a sine qua non of practice in the region. The tragic events of this particular day drove that lesson home once more.

The case history was classic. On their way from Britain to a posting at the Gilgil Army Base in the Rift Valley the newly-weds had opted for one night at Treetops Hotel in Aberdare National Park, made famous in 1953 as the spot where Princess Elizabeth learned of her accession to the throne on the sudden death of her father, King George VI. There was no malaria in Nairobi and none in the Gilgil area, they had been assured of that fact. An overnight stay at Treetops would be a lot of fun and a fine way to cap off their recent honeymoon. After developing a minor fever and then a persistent headache, she had been assured by the medical officer that there was nothing to worry about. 'Just a mild flu,' he said, not taking the trouble to double-check their movements – a fatal mistake. All it needs is one night; all it needs is one bite. The voice on the phone was full of concern:

'It just seemed to be an ordinary flu... but she became suddenly confused this morning and looks very ill now. The ambulance is on its way. Surely it can't be malaria, they've only just arrived in the country.'

The importance of a good history. How many times had that been drilled into us as students. Here was a supreme example. One question omitted and his patient was dying, the reportedly confused state having turned to profound coma by the time the ambulance arrived in Nakuru, the consequence of the malarial parasites now packing the blood vessels in her brain. She died, in fact, less than ten minutes after arrival, with barely a chance for us to do anything except prepare some intravenous quinine, the first and only case of cerebral malaria which I ever encountered and one I can never forget.

Nowadays the picture has changed dramatically. Prophylaxis and treatment are both much more difficult, with the parasites widely resistant to many of the anti-malarial drugs. Cerebral malaria has become more common, my brother telling me in the 1980s that it could sometimes account for more than fifty percent of the admissions to the Intensive Care Unit at the Aga Khan Hospital in Mombasa. With the anophelene mosquito somehow acquiring an ability to survive at higher altitudes, up country populations with no natural immunity are now exposed to a totally new scourge and no region of the country can be said to be malaria-free. That early case stands out from my own time there, along with two others. The diagnosis in the first of these can be best described as a long range one.

Doug Charlton and I were walking up the ramp at the outpatient entrance, a morning's work in the operating room ahead. He pointed up at a row of clearly visible urine specimens. The narrow glass tubes were a hundred and fifty feet away at least, standing as they often did on the windowsill of a small second floor room. 'Looks like someone has blackwater fever.'

I complimented him on his observation, never thinking for a moment that the specimen might be from one of my own patients, agreeing at the same time that "black water" seemed an apt description. I had not yet encountered this rare complication of falciparum malaria,[41] characterised by breakdown of red blood cells and the appearance of haemoglobin in the urine.

Doug disappeared into the downstairs changing room; I headed upstairs to check up on the patient I had admitted late the night before with a non-specific fever.

'Did the night staff repeat the smears?' I asked the staff nurse on duty.

Malaria was a prime suspect in any fever of unknown origin in Kenya, and although at over six thousand feet Nakuru was not an endemic area for the disease, routine blood smears were always taken, and repeated if the temperature shot upwards again.

---

41. The most serious type of malaria.

'They've already gone to the lab,' the nurse replied, 'and that interesting urine specimen is the first he has passed since admission. We sent some off to Austin as well. He looks a bit yellow this morning.'

The jaundice was obvious. Had I missed it in the poor light the night before, I wondered, as well as being perhaps a bit cavalier about just another PUO – pyrexia (fever) of unknown origin – one of the few acronyms we used in those days. He looked sicker now, even though his fever was down. After re-examining him thoroughly and talking to Austin Riley at the nearby lab, and with my interest in Doug's observation by now turning into some dismay, I dived down to the operating room to pick his brains. An experienced physician and anaesthetist as well as being a low-handicap golfer, Doug Charlton had spent almost all of his career in the Colonial Health Service. During numerous remote postings in Kenya he had learned to turn his hand to almost anything. I recall hearing him tell the story of how his wife Pauline had stood by his side on one occasion while he reluctantly performed some major abdominal surgery, reading aloud from *Gray's Anatomy* to ensure that his scalpel would follow the correct path! In terms of statistics blackwater fever carried around a thirty percent mortality. Although we were ill-equipped in Nakuru to deal with any case of impending renal failure, with Doug's invaluable help and a later transfer to Nairobi this patient did make a good recovery, a better outcome than in the last of these three cases which I remember so well.

'Get me a priest,' the Belgian kept repeating. 'I want a priest, quickly… I need a priest!'

He had been admitted after the most minor of accidents and was going into profound shock even as we rushed him along the outside corridor and into the ground floor ward. Bunny Griffiths came in to help start a wide bore intravenous line whilst I administered oxygen, but we didn't have today's equipment nor any immediately available blood. As we poured in the saline and Ringer's solution the Belgian simply died, right in front of our eyes, long before we could get him to the operating room to control a massive intra-abdominal haemorrhage. His last request we fulfilled, but only after his demise.

The long-time resident of Africa had been on holiday from the Belgian Congo and in a very slow-moving collision had fallen against an open car door. Within an hour of the accident he was dead. At post-mortem we found that his grossly enlarged and malarial spleen had been completely torn in two. On hearing the story Doug Charlton, playing a different role now as pathologist, had suggested this finding as almost a certainty. Yet another face of malaria. If only we had had more time. Kraus had it right, and Manson's researches didn't dwell on the personal consequences of this fascinating disease. 'This is what you wanted,' I reminded myself; 'Manson and malaria… tropical medicine. Wasn't that what you and that career counsellor talked about at Merchiston?'

THE VIP

For the apparel oft proclaims the man.
Shakespeare

First impressions can be deceiving. Despite a mild fever the visitor was not in bed, but seated with several of our friends at a cluttered and untidy breakfast table. It wasn't the type of setting in which one expected to meet a very important personage, but VIPs are ordinary folk, too, who have to have breakfast like the rest of us before they emerge to face the outside world. With the sleeves of his collarless shirt partly rolled up, he looked little different from the others in the room. Little different, that is, until one met his eyes.

I had been asked to see him quite urgently, although he was not acutely ill. Newly arrived in Africa, though long enough for malaria to be an obvious consideration had he travelled through a suspect area, he felt vaguely unwell and had a raised temperature. With the big ceremony scarcely three days away, my orders came in no uncertain terms: 'You must have him well by then.'

Venturing one or two preliminary questions, I found my eyes held by his. There was a magnetism in those eyes, making it very apparent that while he was quite prepared to be treated as an ordinary patient, this was no ordinary individual.

We got down to the business of medicine. He had arrived in Nairobi the previous weekend and spent a few days at Machakos to the south. Nairobi was malaria free at that time, but Machakos might be another matter. In symptomatic terms it didn't sound like malaria, though blood smears would certainly be necessary; the irritative cough, slight pyrexia, and characteristic sounds over the left lower lobe favoured other probabilities. A chest x-ray at the Nakuru War Memorial Hospital didn't take long to organise, with a stop at Austin Riley's lab on the way. There was clearly no point in telling him he should go to bed.

'Probably an early pneumonia,' I told his hosts.

'Will he be fit enough for Eldoret?' they asked immediately.

The visitor answered for me, his unfamiliar American accent suddenly more obvious. 'The Doc here will fix me up... I'll be just fine by Saturday.'

His tone left no room for debate. Having come all this way for the big occasion, a touch of pneumonia wasn't about to slow him up.

That was my introduction to a man who possessed the most charismatic personality I have ever known, let alone encountered in a patient. Whether in a large gathering or a small group, whether surrounded by dignitaries or common folk, the Most Reverend Fulton J. Sheen, Auxiliary Bishop of New York and National Director for the World Mission Society for the Propagation of the Faith, could hold any listener in the palm of his hand.

A few days later, in the presence it seemed of every black and white member of the Catholic hierarchy of East and West Africa, and giving little outward sign that he still did not feel entirely well, he was the principal celebrant at the consecration of Joseph B. Houlihan as Bishop of the Diocese of Eldoret. The two-hour long ceremony took place in a large open field, with Betty and I among the large crowd. While a huge canopy gave some protection to the main participants, none of the rest of us had any respite from the strengthening morning sun.

I remember the occasion particularly because of its colour. A cloudless blue sky, the white habits of scores of priests and nuns, the predominantly black laity, splashes of red everywhere with monsignors, bishops and a Nigerian cardinal in striking contrast to Fulton Sheen's own green vestments. We still treasure a clear memory of parts of his sermon. Speaking in English and pausing frequently to allow Archbishop McCarthy of Nairobi to translate each section into Swahili, he employed many simple similes and metaphors to get his message across, likening faith to water flowing from a faucet, an unfamiliar term at that time to our European ears, always provided that the faucet (tap) had the requisite connection to Christ.

The crowd spilled around at the end, reluctant to leave in spite of the heat. As we stood talking to Paddy Cullen, one of our good friends from the St Patrick's Missionary Fathers, we heard a loud shout and the by now familiar accent: 'There's my doctor... and Betty... I'll be right over.'

We chatted for a while, Paddy making a record of the occasion for us with his camera, before other obligations drew him away into the huge gathering around us.

It remains one of the privileges of our time in Africa to have met and talked with Fulton Sheen, to have had him personally inscribe for us a copy of his remarkable story of the life of Christ[42] and to have received a further letter from him a few years before his death in 1979. Whatever the cause or institution, only rarely does a truly outstanding advocate appear. Fulton Sheen's place in such company is secure. He represented the very antithesis of Shakespeare's well-known saying, for he needed none of the outward trappings of his office in order to be clearly recognised as a VIP.

---

42. Sheen, Fulton J. *Life of Christ*. Surrey, Peter Davies, 1959.

A DIFFICULT DECISION

Because the newer methods of treatment are good,
it does not follow that the old ones were bad:
for if our honourable and worshipful ancestors
had not recovered from their ailments,
you and I would not be alive today.
attributed to Confucius

Each of these last few stories have involved problems in diagnosis, a term derived from the Greek words for "through" and "knowledge". The etymology of the related term *prognosis*, meaning "a telling beforehand" or "to know beforehand", is similarly based, and more broadly accepted since the time of Hippocrates as the ability to foretell the probable course and outcome of a disease. There are pitfalls in every prognosis, however, and lessons to be learned, as illustrated by the following case. Although it has nothing to do with Kenya it has everything to do with the lessons of medicine.

The year is 1943. The place, a small twenty-bed hospital in Surrey, England. A young boy of eight is gravely ill. He has been bedridden for eight months, suffering from what was then called nephrosis (later termed the nephrotic syndrome), a form of chronic kidney disease, with restriction of fluids, a salt-free, high-protein diet and urea as a diuretic the only available treatment regime. Everything indicates the onset of the terminal stage of the disease. For the past few months the boy has required frequent and distressing needle aspirations to remove accumulated fluid from his abdomen. Now in a uraemic coma, with his body grossly swollen, he is paralysed on one side of his body and has a severe chest infection.

Round his bedside sit three physicians. The first is the boy's father, the second his family doctor, a close friend, and the third a specialist from London, Dr Horace Evans, who has brought with him a new drug called mersalyl, a mercurial diuretic, never before used in Britain in such a case. He warns that this new agent could well have a fatal effect. The three physicians struggle with the decision. Will they merely be condemning him to a longer period of terminal suffering? After much agonising discussion the injection is given by the very distressed family doctor.

A dying patient with no foreseeable future. A new drug or treatment, which might kill or cure, but one which may also prolong unnecessary suffering. How best to solve the dilemma in the interest of the patient and his family? That was 1943. Yet it could just as easily be the year 2010. Although the clinical circumstances may be different, the journals and newspapers of today are full of similar sorts of cases. The central issues simply do not change.

The first is an obvious one, that the outcome of any clinical situation is never predictable. This young patient started to pass urine within an hour of the injection of mersalyl, continuing to do little else for the next week. He rapidly regained consciousness, the paralysis proving temporary. As the accumulated fluids poured away his father described his appearance as becoming almost like a skeleton. Even more surprisingly, although gross proteinuria[43] continued for a number of years, the boy went on to make a complete recovery from his illness, all residual signs of renal disease disappearing following a tonsillectomy in 1946. Prior to spending a scientific research year in Antarctica in 1960 he passed an extensive medical examination and continues in excellent health to this day.

A second lesson is that clinical decisions and methods of treatment can only be made within the boundaries of existing knowledge. In 1943 steroids had not yet arrived on the therapeutic scene; they became the mainstay of the management of the nephrotic syndrome. The early kidney machines, too, were three to four years away, with renal dialysis and kidney transplants still beyond a distant horizon. Not only will treatment regimes change dramatically with the passage of time, but many will come to be regarded as being totally flawed. When "The Doctor" discussed his son's illness in a letter to the *British Medical Journal* in the mid 1970s – for this patient is my first cousin – another letter from three prominent paediatricians on the same issue stressed the danger of the use of diuretics in the nephrotic syndrome. Yet in this case almost three hundred injections of the mercurial diuretic were given over a period of three years! My uncle's letter included the following words:

> *Had steroids been available in 1942, the treatment in this case would never have been used, but the result confirms that proteinuria in itself is not injurious provided it is controlled by diuretics. One other interesting fact emerged during this illness. It was noticed that the intake of white meat always increased the urinary output. When we were able to obtain a chicken or a rabbit, although the*

---

43. Loss of protein in the urine.

fluid intake remained constant, the patient's urinary output always increased, so that the intervals between the injections of the diuretic could be prolonged.

Whatever the experts might also have said – then or now – about the final combination of events, the tonsillectomy and subsequent remission of the nephrosis, to the end of his life my uncle remained firmly convinced that they had been cause and effect. I'd give anything to be able to discuss all these things with him one more time, for there is a further lesson in this case, as we will see, one with wider roots and still wider implications.

LIVING AND LEARNING
THE ROAD TO MOMBASA

It ain't the driving as 'urts 'em,
it's the 'ammer, 'ammer, 'ammer along the 'ard 'igh road.
adapted from *Punch*, 1856

The *Guinness Book of Records* was in its comparative infancy in the early 1960s, largely restricted in content to the recording of sporting achievements. Nowadays it comes in many different volumes, a major industry in fact, with all the world vying for a place amongst its pages. Had my wife Betty and I known of this future development we could perhaps have forwarded a claim from our honeymoon, a claim that would surely have been no less ridiculous than some of today's artificial records.

We were married by Bishop Houlihan in the small Benedictine convent in Nakuru, afterwards welcoming a larger gathering under the huge pepper trees in the garden of my mother's home. Our oldest guest is worth a special mention. By then a widow in her nineties, at the beginning of the century Miss Sim had taught my father and his brothers at West Bridgend Primary School in Dumbarton.

Making our escape early on the Saturday afternoon, Betty and I drove the hundred or so miles to Nairobi on what was then Kenya's only tarmac road, arriving in time for a twilight glimpse of a pride of lions in the Nairobi National Park. After a night at the Norfolk Hotel, a relic of colonial Kenya which was later destroyed in a fire, we set off on the long journey to Mombasa. Just three hundred miles, not very far by today's travelling standards, but then a tedious day-long journey on a pothole-strewn red murram road. The euphoria of the morning did not last for long.

Soon after leaving Nairobi, short of the Athi River, we turned off the main road and headed towards a sign indicating the presence of a petrol station. In the excitement of the previous day we had forgotten the obvious necessity of a fill-up. As we prepared to leave the small duka some ten minutes later we spotted a totally flat back tire. This having been duly changed, we enquired as to the nearest spot down the road where the puncture could be repaired. As we got back into the car, Betty exclaimed: 'My train case has gone! It was sitting there on the floor in front of the seat a moment ago. Someone has stolen it. All our money… my passport, my bracelet and charms… everything is in that case!'

The Indian duka owner disclaimed any responsibility, and simply shrugged his shoulders: 'Must have been one of the Africans who were lolling about. You'll never get it back.'

I knew that my new wife was a pretty determined sort of person. She underlined it that morning, refusing to leave until the case was returned. We cajoled, remonstrated and argued, finally threatening to fetch the police from Machakos. A dignified looking headman eventually appeared and a prolonged bilingual discussion began. Although he gave no indication of his feelings he must have been worried about our threats, for some minutes after he had retired towards his village we saw a young African coming slowly towards us, the red and white train case in his hand. The lock had been forced, but absolutely nothing was missing. We surmised the reason. A metal crucifix lay on the top of the contents, large enough to cause a thief some second-guessing about the consequences of exploration. Reflecting that this was not the best way to have started our honeymoon, but nevertheless breathing a large sigh of relief, we headed back to the main road. Our troubles were only beginning, however, which brings me back to the question of records.

What do you suppose is the record for the most punctures on the first day of a honeymoon? Whatever figure you might suggest, I would claim that we exceeded it on that journey to Mombasa. We had barely had the first repair completed than we were forced to return to the same garage for a second time, and from then on the five tyres of my Vauxhall Victor appeared to compete with each other as to which of them should collapse first. Somehow we managed to avoid the dangerous nightmare of being stranded on the road with two airless tyres and it was well after dark by the time we staggered into Mombasa. In today's Kenya we might not have escaped unscathed.

After a memorable first look at the Indian Ocean in the morning we headed up the coast towards Malindi, the holiday mecca of the East African coast. Miraculously the tyres held out and we lazed away the next ten days at the beachfront Sinbad Hotel. Malindi was extremely hot and humid, causing us both to develop prickly heat, not the most romantic complaint to develop on one's honeymoon! The town was packed with tourists,[44] with one familiar Scots face in a lunchtime throng. The story of my re-acquaintance with this individual is worth telling.

Some months earlier my brother Graham and I had been passing a few hours away on the balcony of the Rift Valley Sports Club in Nakuru, watching a cricket match between the locals and an Army eleven. I became absorbed by the action of

---

44. In sad contrast to our return to the town in 1987.

one of the opposition's slow bowlers. 'That chap bowls exactly like Peter Welsh used to do at Cambusdoon,' I remarked, referring to the star bowler at our small school.

'You couldn't possibly remember a bowling action after all this time,' Graham snorted. 'You were only fourteen then and we haven't heard anything of the Welsh family for years. That was Ayrshire and this is East Africa!'

I persisted with my speculation, and wandering over to the scorer's box during the tea interval we found the familiar name, Captain P. M. Welsh. Graham had barely stopped shaking his head by the time we searched Peter out. We reminisced for a while about the war years at school when his French mother had taught us her native tongue. Now four months later here he was in Malindi, staying overnight at our honeymoon hotel. I've never seen him since.

But all honeymoons have to come to an end. Driving back to Nairobi I speculated that the Victor's tyre problem might have originated on another rough Kenyan road, the road to Ortum in the Suk valley in the north-west of the country. Our friend Tom Grennan had gone there to recuperate from an illness and we were invited for a long weekend. The two hundred-odd miles from Nakuru through Eldoret and Kitale was a fair drive on the murram surface, with elevations at times to over nine thousand feet. The next section to Ortum was pretty much a road to the middle of the back of beyond, if not quite to nowhere, with large boulders to be negotiated and countless descents into far from empty river beds. We were lucky to get stuck only once or twice and with no contingency plans of any kind perhaps even more fortunate that our wheels did not bog down completely. Betty had strong legs and arms, however. She did all of the pushing and we got there in the end before the light had begun to fade.

Although the Suk remained a backward tribe, clinging to many ancient customs and taboos, the Catholic Mission at Ortum was very much alive and well, run by a priest from the St Patrick's Missionary Society and five Irish Sisters of the Holy Rosary Order. Somewhat bare inside, the stone church displayed a surprisingly attractive exterior, a tribute to the industry of that isolated valley.

Sister Cabrini had total charge of the small hospital, perhaps even of the whole Mission. A fully trained surgeon with her Irish Fellowship, she took us on a fascinating ward round. With enlarged livers or spleens to be palpated at almost every bed, we seemed to be turning the pages of a textbook of tropical medicine. I remember two young patients particularly, severe cases of kwashiorkor, a condition which I had not previously seen. The curious name is derived from the language of a Ghanaian tribe, meaning "the disease the first child gets when the second is on the way", the syndrome itself due to extreme lack of dietary protein and everything associated with such a situation.

Cases of active tuberculosis were nursed on an open balcony along one side of the hospital building, their only protection from the heavy late afternoon rains provided by individual heavy tarpaulins draped from the roof. Sister Cabrini enthused over her job, her frequent safaris by truck to the outlying districts, and the new hospital building shortly due to open. We laughed when shown the Outpatient Department, a large tree where patients congregated daily, hanging up their belongings and passing waiting hours in conversation with friends, a situation hardly likely to be accepted in our own culture.

Some distance from the hospital lay the few imported-stone buildings which housed the priests and nuns, the one belonging to the latter very attractively land-scaped. Standing beside them in the bright Kenyan sun for photographs, with the always gorgeous flat-topped thorn trees dotted around the landscape, one could imagine the location idyllic. The reality differed. Although giving great respect to the spirit of the individual, the Suk people held great fear of a death in their midst, a fact which frequently led them to abandon aged and dying relatives to the bush and to the "mercy" of scavenging hyenas. Not many halcyon days therefore, but rather days and weeks and months of unremitting hard work, that was the pattern of life at the Ortum Mission. It might be fun to go back for a return visit, if only to see how the Outpatient Department had progressed into the new century!

Looking back at the demands of the mixed general and anaesthetic practice I ran in Nakuru, I doubt if many of today's young physicians would tolerate the work load, on call for twenty-four hours a day and seven days a week. Although thinking more and more about my need of further studies in anaesthesia, I now had significantly greater practical experience in this area than the others doctors in the town. My hours in the operating room lengthened steadily, without any compensatory reduction in the numbers of general and obstetric cases, and the loss of a night's sleep with a full day still to come was an occasional occurrence. In terms of job satisfaction it represented the best of all worlds, with specialist help always readily available. If any of my maternity patients required a Caesarean delivery I only had to look after "the upper end" of the table and let someone else worry about the surgery. I had never, ever, wanted to be a surgeon.

We saw many fascinating cases, some of which are strange to think back on now with the benefit of hindsight. The hospital kept no banked blood, just a panel of potential donors to be called on in any emergency, listed by blood groups. In practice it was not always easy to persuade them to fulfil their commitment, particularly in the middle of the night. The system worked pretty well, however, giving our small community hospital one specific advantage over today's major centres. This is well illustrated by the story of a road traffic accident involving one of my own obstetric patients.

Some twenty-four weeks pregnant and in good health, she occupied the front passenger seat in a car returning to Nakuru. An early evening collision – no seat belts in those days – caused a direct blow to her abdomen. Premature contractions had begun by the time we admitted her to hospital and after a very rapid labour the baby was born dead, the placenta appearing almost immediately with significant bleeding and large clots. For some time after the birth she seemed fine, but then her blood pressure began to fall, with indications of intra-abdominal bleeding. Austin Riley sent out a call for blood donors and we headed for the operating room. It proved to be a long night, particularly for the surgeon, Johnnie Johnston, who was far from well. No sooner had he identified one source of bleeding than another would start up and the patient even began to bleed from her urinary tract. We persevered over a good few hours, however, and after the transfusion of four or five pints of blood the bleeding slowed down and then stopped altogether. Johnnie closed the abdomen with relief. I found him in the washroom shortly afterwards, retching and vomiting. It proved to be the last operation he ever performed, pancreatic cancer claiming him a few months later.

As for the patient, she looked fine the following morning. 'Sounds like afibrinogenaemia,' said our obstetrician, Geoff Bird, who had not been involved the night before. The proof sat on the window sill of the operating room, one of several specimens of blood I had taken for cross matching during the night. Six hours later and still no sign of clotting. Somewhat unwittingly, of course, we had cured her. Fresh whole blood, administered while still warm from the donors, is full of all the missing factors for coagulation. Although seldom if ever available these days, in such a situation it remains the best of all treatments. "Afibrinogenaemia" as we called it, a lack of clotting factors in practical terms, became known later under the different term of "disseminated intravascular coagulopathy". In our particular patient it had been triggered by the bleeding behind the placenta, the mechanism of which I was still woefully ignorant.

Betty and I began to talk about returning to the UK and about my choosing to enter the speciality I had despised as a medical student. There were many sides to the decision. It would mean a return to junior hospital posts, to a great deal of study and several years of financial uncertainty, for contrary to common public perception full training in anaesthesia is the equal in every way to that demanded of a would-be surgeon. Kenya was heading for independence with *Uhuru Sasa*[45] beginning to appear on crudely constructed signs, and with political instability a probability the country might not prove the best place to start our hoped for family. Leaving Nakuru meant quite a wrench, for it had been an almost ideal place to live and practise: a near perfect climate with no tropical heat and predictable rains; Nakuru Golf Club

---

45. Swahili for "Freedom Now".

on the side of Menengai, with its panoramic view of the township and Lake and of the gorgeous surrounding countryside; three racially separated hospitals, however much such an arrangement would now be questioned, with a fascinating patient mix of tropical and non-tropical disease; having a one-on-one relationship with every individual to whom I gave an anaesthetic; working closely with my wife, the nurse in charge of the operating room at the European hospital; and practising family medicine in a comparatively small community in an era when personal service to patients remained paramount and when physicians had not yet begun to look over their shoulders at their colleagues' comparative earnings.

Many memories of patients from those days remain, with a small coincidental group certainly worth a final mention. A tale of three wives, in fact: one of a local farmer, the second of one of the local surgeons, and the third the wife of a good friend.

The first lady was booked by Geoff Bird for a repeat Caesarean section and he had asked me to give the anaesthetic. As she lived some way out of town, with roads which could be questionable in the event of early evening rains, Geoff had given her strict instructions about the danger of delay should any signs of impending labour occur ahead of the operation date. Heeding this advice to the letter, she and her husband duly made it into town during the stage of early uterine contractions. The prospect of ten days of hospital food troubled this particular expectant mother, however, so she decided they should go to the Rift Valley Sports Club for a last decent meal, presenting at the hospital an hour and a half later in active labour and with a very full stomach. Although not everyone might understand that this is the worst of combinations for an immediately required general anaesthetic for a Caesarean section, for a highly intelligent individual it constituted remarkably stupid behaviour. Fortunately for both of us, she held on to her four course dinner until moments after an uneventful recovery to full consciousness. I should add that at this point in my career I had no experience in either spinal or epidural anaesthesia.

The second lady was in her late fifties, due to have an elective cholecystectomy (removal of her gall-bladder). Apart from being somewhat overweight she could be classed as a good anaesthetic risk in every way except one – her husband's unfortunate and very unusual marital history. He had lost two previous spouses in West Africa in the past, the cause of death identical on each occasion, a sudden embolus (blood clot) to the lungs in the recovery period following a cholecystectomy, almost certainly a consequence of the prolonged post-operative bed rest which was common practice at that time. There was considerable apprehension, as can well be imagined, and few post-operative patients in those days can ever have found themselves mobilised so quickly. A bottle of the best Scotch whisky arrived at my office a few days after her safe discharge from hospital.

Our suitcases were packed and my practice otherwise closed down when the time came to look after the last of these three wives, to assist her in the completely normal delivery of a healthy girl. Having good friends as patients was an upbeat note to leave on. Betty and I took such a fancy to their car, one of the latest Vauxhall Victors, immaculate in white with red upholstery, that we traded in our old grey Victor against an identical model for delivery in London. We discussed the possibility of a meeting at some time in the future, for they were also planning to leave Kenya. In the event it was many months before we heard anything more about them. A passenger in a horrendous car crash in Ireland, my very last patient in Africa, so happy with her new baby when we had left her, had been thrown through the windshield and killed.

Explanation of peri-operative risk is paramount today, with outcomes subject to as many factors as in life itself. Here were three women in good health. In one the major hazard came from her own actions, in the next the concern with which she approached the proposed surgery understandably lay in her own mind, while the last tragic aftermath to a normal pregnancy rested simply in the hands of fate. Timely reminders of the fragility of all of our lives.

Before the flight home there still remained time for an overnight visit to the famous Treetops Hotel. Although I had to pay heavily for the privilege a few days later in the Customs Hall at Heathrow, I managed to capture some of the images with a new 8 mm cine camera: a brief glimpse of the cloud covered peak of Mount Kenya on the way; the crude escape tree-ladders on the track leading towards Treetops; the rifle of our guide in the ready position; and the timid warthogs and inquisitive baboons, the latter eagerly clambering onto the roof-top balcony to greet us. After a fine evening meal we were wakened during the night to watch the arrival of a herd of elephants. The bewitching sounds of an African night come at you from all sides. Whether you stay or leave, they are never forgotten. Hard to imagine we had chosen to replace them with the noise of the crowded London streets.

A HALLOWED HALL

Examinations are formidable even to the best prepared,
for the greatest fool can ask more than the wisest man can
answer.
Charles Caleb Colton (1780-1832)

Generations of physicians passed through the portals of the old Examination Hall at Queen's Square in central London, a necessary ritual for most of the twentieth century for aspiring specialists seeking the approval of the Royal Colleges. Success at Queen's Square could lead to the opening of many doors, even towards fame and fortune for a few, whilst failure would mean further months of study and return visits, or perhaps a lifetime of disappointment.

I had no great qualms as I arrived there one Saturday morning in 1963. After three months of extra evening classes with Professor R. J. Last I felt I had covered the ground for the anatomy portion of the Primary Fellowship Exam in Anaesthesia several times. Only a third of the candidates normally passed at the first attempt, not an encouraging figure, but everyone knew that Last's students averaged almost double that success rate. With a wife and now a small baby at home, and not much money in the bank, it was not an exam I could afford to fail.

The paper containing the essay-type questions lay face down on the desk. I glanced around, waiting for the bell to signal the start of the allotted three hours. There were no familiar faces in my immediate vicinity, but I knew that my fellow registrars Jim and Bill must be out there somewhere. 'Go for the easiest question first,' I reminded myself; 'Rough out the answers first, and divide your time up properly.' Professor Last was a stickler for good exam technique.

The invigilator's hand descended on his bell. An audible rustle followed as the two hundred or so candidates turned over their paper. I looked at the first question with some puzzlement:

Describe the origin, course and distribution of Morrison's nerve.

The exam always contained a question couched in those terms, usually concerning one of the twelve cranial nerves, the nerves which originate inside the skull, but occasionally asking about a peripheral nerve of importance in anaesthesia. But Morrison's nerve? I had never heard of it. The only Morrison I could think of was Andrew Morrison, the ear, nose and throat surgeon at Whipps Cross Hospital, and the name did not appear in Last's textbook of anatomy, I felt certain of that. Everyone around me appeared to be writing furiously, while I remained paralysed, staring at the paper, mesmerised by that first question. Like those of a drowning man my thoughts flashed by. Our return from a comparatively comfortable income in East Africa; the plan to go into full time anaesthesia, building on the marvellous practical experience Kenya had given me; our hopes for enlarging our family. Everything was going up in smoke and I could only sit and stare: 'Get on with rest of the exam,' I told myself; 'You'll remember in a moment. This is ridiculous. You must know what Morrison's nerve is. You must…'

But I didn't. And I couldn't function either, looking at my watch for the umpteenth time as the minutes flashed by. Some people had even begun to leave the hall. I hadn't even started writing. 'My God, only half an hour left… what a disaster,' I told myself. Then suddenly, as if by magic, or as though they had been written in invisible ink, three additional words appeared…

Describe the origin, course and distribution of Morrison's nerve (the pudendal nerve)[46]

'Good grief, why did I not see that before?' I almost shouted at myself, beginning to write furiously. The bell sounded as I was on my second line. The exam was finished. So was I. An ignominious failure after all that work. How on earth would I break the news to Betty? Only then did I realise that I wasn't in Queen's Square at all. I was looking up at the white bedroom ceiling of our South Woodford home, totally drenched in sweat. I can honestly say that I have never had a more vivid nightmare, every bit of it clearly remembered to this day. With the exam still three days away I took a few deep breaths. Lots of time still to review the anatomy of the pudendal nerve, amongst other things, if I could pull my scattered wits together.

By the time I got to Queen's Square the following Tuesday I had the pudendal nerve off by heart, taking a final look at my notes on the thirty minute journey on the Underground from South Woodford. This time I recognised a few of the faces in the crowd. I wished Bill luck. He didn't look too happy.

The same bell rang, followed by the same rustling. I looked at the first question once more:

---

46. The pudendal nerve is important in obstetric anaesthesia.

*Describe the origin, course and distribution of the pudendal nerve
in the female.*

I could hardly believe my luck, but didn't hesitate, barely stopping to think. Within thirty minutes I had every single fact written down. Three questions still to go and two and a half hours remaining, lots of time. Nine out of ten for sure on that particular question, perhaps even ten if the examiners might ever be so generous. It turned into the easiest exam of my life.

Jim looked downcast. 'My anatomy cramming didn't get below the diaphragm,' he muttered sadly. 'I could only manage a few lines on the pudendal nerve. I've failed for sure.' Bill voiced similar feelings, although in much more succinct terms. My own thoughts centred on the power of one's subconscious mind. I later discovered that the pudendal nerve had not been asked in the primary fellowship in anaesthesia for more than twenty years. Yet my brain had somehow projected the approximate ten to one odds of a question on a peripheral rather than a cranial nerve, highlighting at the same time the possibility of the pudendal nerve, akin to a Grand National outsider coming in at odds of a hundred to one. On such things may one's life turn. I don't think that Jim ever did get the exam, while Bill made it only after several attempts. They had not had my advantage of a place in Professor Last's anatomy course, held during evenings and weekends at the Royal College of Surgeons in Lincoln's Inn Fields. While Last remains the only regular snuff-user I have ever met, there were no quirks in his teaching. He was totally committed at every tutorial and prided himself on the success of his students.

There was no time to rest on any laurels following the first part of the Fellowship exam, however, for the second part still lay ahead, with essay-type papers on anaesthesia, medicine, surgery and pharmacology followed by long and short clinical cases and finally by the dreaded vivas – eye to eye across a table with two separate pairs of the big names in British anaesthesia.[47] Patients still react with surprise when they discover that we have gone through the same extensive training as our surgical colleagues, making nonsense of the question a good friend and colleague of mine was once asked on the golf course: 'Are you a doctor or just an anaesthetist?'

It is strange to look back on those days of study now, based as one of three Anaesthetic Registrars at Whipps Cross Hospital in the north-east of London and later as Senior Registrar at Kingston upon Thames. With the help of Ken Slack and the late Norman Eve, two of the four consultants at Whipps Cross, I was introduced for the first time to the concept of balanced anaesthesia, to mechanical ventilators, to

---

47. I still have all the papers from those 1960s exams and also a note of every topic covered in the clinical and oral sessions. I wouldn't like to have to try to answer any of them now!

spinal and epidural analgesia and to many other elements of a very different speciality than the one I had previously known. Forty and more years later it is fascinating to look back at some of the cases we had, in particular at the limitations placed on our management by the knowledge of the day.

Bill Chew and I had just finished a full morning giving anaesthetics for urology. Before heading for lunch we thought we should pay a quick visit to the ward to check on our last patient, since he had lost rather more blood than usual during a prostatectomy under combined general and epidural anaesthesia. Post-operative cases were returned directly from the operating rooms to large open wards, their beds placed nearest to the nursing stations where vital signs might be carefully watched. Once awake, however, in order to shelter other patients from the unpleasant sights or sounds which could be part of the early recovery period, they were often surrounded by portable screens. We found the first bed on the right so sheltered and stepping behind the curtains our immediate impression was that the man was dead. Supported in the semi-upright position by a number of pillows, he looked as white as a sheet, did not appear to be breathing and had no palpable pulse. Bill grabbed a chair as I removed the pillows and together we yanked up the bottom of the bed, placing the chair seat under it. We turned our attention then to the patient's airway and were rewarded with a typical "thankful" sigh. A faint pulse reappeared, followed by a tinge of colour to the face, subsequent oxygen administration and a rapid intravenous infusion soon completing the recovery. Another minute or two and we would have been too late. Such were the perils of having no recovery rooms. We were learning the science of anaesthesia, but in other respects there was still a long way to go.

Intensive care units were only in a gestational stage at that time, cardiac monitors few and far between, the technology of blood gases measurement just beginning to appear and the vitally important significance of the body's acid-base balance poorly understood. I remember one very ill patient who appeared to breathe well at the end of an emergency abdominal operation, only to deteriorate rapidly and die shortly after his return to the ward. Just one week later we heard a landmark paper on metabolic acidosis at an anaesthetic meeting in London. Its presenter described in almost exact detail the clinical picture exhibited by our patient, and more importantly the manner in which we could have treated and possibly saved him.

A year or more later we had a related post-operative death, one which by then should certainly have been preventable. It marked the first operation for an aortic aneurysm carried out at Whipps Cross, performed by the young vascular surgeon Louis De Jode who had recently been appointed to the staff. As the registrar on duty I assisted Norman Eve with the anaesthesia. The operation took some five hours, starting around two am, and went well in every respect, the patient being awake and stable on his return to the ward. We all felt pretty pleased with ourselves, I remember, as we headed for early breakfasts in our respective homes. With another full day in the OR in prospect, despite being up all night, I had to be back at the hospital to prepare for the nine o'clock start. I went to the ward to check on our patient, only to be told by the house surgeon that he had died around eight.

'What on earth happened?' I asked him. 'Did you call Mr De Jode or Dr Eve?'

A host of questions surfaced, mostly answered in the negative. When the patient's condition started to deteriorate soon after our departure the young doctor had taken everything on himself. What made it so upsetting was that his description of an individual with increasing respiratory difficulty mirrored our earlier case. We were by now well aware of the metabolic changes associated with extended cross-clamping of the aorta and the infusion of major amounts of stored blood, and although lacking the capability to track these changes, had followed the recommended regime of bicarbonate replacement. After such a major and new procedure it remains incredible that neither the surgeon nor any of those who had spent the whole night working with this patient were informed of the change in his condition. No recovery rooms, no "crash carts", no intensive care units, but respiratory support possible with an anaesthetic machine just yards from the patient's bedside. Particularly disappointing was the fact that post-mortem examination showed the surgical repair of the aorta to be intact.

Even the day of the week can stay in one's memory of a particular case. Andrew Doughty and I arrived one Friday to start an afternoon's list in the Gynaecology theatre at Kingston, where I had moved to continue my final year of training. We found that an extra patient had been added and placed first on the list. Neither of us had seen this thirty-nine-year-old lady before her arrival in the operating room. Significant hypertension in the first weeks of her pregnancy, continuing and worsening by the thirtieth week, had led to a regime of complete bed rest in hospital as she awaited the birth of her first child. She was noted to have cutaneous neurofibromatosis. After an initial period with a relatively labile blood pressure, her condition had remained stable until the thirty-eighth week of her pregnancy, when her blood pressure began to climb again, a trace of albumin appearing in her urine for the first time. As an elderly primigravida with the breech the presenting part, there were a number of good reasons for the decision to perform an immediate Caesarean section.

About three minutes after the routine induction of anaesthesia her pulse rate suddenly rose to over two hundred and the blood pressure became unrecordable. Acute pulmonary oedema developed shortly after the delivery of a live female infant and although the child did well all subsequent efforts to restore the mother's condition proved unsuccessful, the resuscitation being finally abandoned some ninety minutes after the start of the operation.

Such a scenario is the anaesthetist's worst nightmare. We suspected the reason even before the post-mortem supplied it, a phaeochromocytoma, the rare tumour of the adrenal gland which is a major anaesthetic hazard at the best of times due to its potential for releasing dangerous levels of the hormones of that gland. When undiagnosed the problems are compounded. My thoughts went back to a previous occasion at Whipps Cross when Ken Slack had successfully opted for a combination of epidural and general anaesthesia for the removal of a similar but known tumour. The particularly unfortunate thing about the lack of a diagnosis in the Kingston case lay in the fact that I afterwards found many reports in the literature of an association between neurofibromatosis and phaeochromocytoma, some from as far back as 1913.[48] Despite these reports, no reference to this association could be found in any of the then current British textbooks of anaesthesia and scant reference only in those of other specialities, nor to the potential hazard when a patient with neurofibromatosis presents for operation. Had this association been known to any of those concerned with the care of this patient the correct diagnosis would have been made during her seven-week hospital stay.

Another day of the week remembered, the patient this time a curly fair-headed girl of about five or six. With an unexpected Thursday morning off I got the chance to observe a series of short dental anaesthetics in a number of different locations in the Kingston district. The morning's eight patients all sat upright in the dental chair, where they inhaled a mixture of nitrous oxide and oxygen, nothing more, given by a very experienced dental anaesthetist. At the end of this particular brief procedure the dentist turned to me and commented on how smoothly it had gone. But neither he, nor the anaesthetist, had seen what I had seen, standing slightly behind the head of the dental chair, and neither could understand why the young girl took more than half an hour to wake up. One of her hands had started to twitch in seizure-like fashion during the induction, continuing to do so until after the extraction of the last tooth, certain evidence of a period of unsuspected cerebral hypoxia. My career-long concern over this method of dental anaesthesia began that morning. Although a good friend can counter with a large series of uneventful personal cases, I had the added privilege of having met and assisted the late Dr J. G. Bourne, regarded as something of a maverick in the UK in the sixties and seventies because of his views on this subject.[49] He advised against the upright position, espousing an alternative technique for short procedures using cyclopropane. That this method did not meet with the full approval of the nursing sister in charge of the day recovery unit at Bournemouth General Hospital is an understatement. I was doing a short locum there, not long after getting back from Kenya, and I still remember her opinion of one morning's work. 'Where's Dr Bourne?

48. Humble, R. M. "Phaeochromocytoma, neurofibromatosis and pregnancy." *Anaesthesia* 1967; **22**, 2: 296-303.

49. Bourne, J. G. *Nitrous Oxide in Dentistry – Its Danger and Alternatives*. London, Lloyd-Luke, 1960.

I'll kill him… I'll kill him!' she kept on repeating as she moved from one retching and vomiting patient to the next. I corresponded with Dr Bourne about dental anaesthesia in later years but never told him where he had come on that day's popularity poll.

With nearly a thousand beds, and also the busy obstetric unit at nearby Forest Gate Hospital, Whipps Cross had proved a fortunate choice as a training ground. Norman Eve and Ken Slack used equally sound though often almost diametrically opposed methods in their anaesthetic practice, giving me early evidence of the fact that there can be more than one way of giving a good anaesthetic for the same operation. Their names have an honoured place in my book of thanks alongside the teachers of my youth. Ken's forward thinking also brought us the unique learning experience of working with a single patient hyperbaric oxygen chamber, only the second to come into use in the United Kingdom at that time. In Kingston, too, I was lucky to work under Andrew Doughty, already a leader in epidural analgesia and then making early moves towards a major involvement in intensive and coronary care. Of social and demographic interest from those joint times was the fact that while ruptured diverticulitis followed acute appendicitis as the commonest cause of an acute abdominal emergency in north-east London, perforated peptic ulcers took that second place in the more prosperous Kingston to the south and west – different incomes, different lifestyles, different diets.[50]

While the city of London offered its postgraduate students a wealth of professional opportunities and meetings, it also held many other attractions. Betty and I were living in a rented apartment at South Woodford, in a building which was later swallowed up by the expansion of the north London motorways, and though off-duty excursions were rationed following the arrival of our first daughter we did manage an occasional evening out. With Lionel Bart at his zenith and Noel Coward winding down, we enjoyed the total contrast of their respective musicals *Blitz* and *Sail Away*, went to one opera, laughed at the antics of Flanders and Swann and chortled over Harry Secombe's performance in *Mr Pickwick*. My golf clubs had been put away due to the combined constraints of finance and study, but I occasionally managed to follow one other outside interest. Half a crown each way at ante-post odds of fifty to one on Monawin, the winner of the 1963 Lincolnshire Handicap, enabled me to buy a painting that Betty had admired in a local gallery window. A couple of weeks later I almost doubled up on the bookies with a similar wager on the Grand National, my selection faltering only yards from the winning post.[51] I dreamt of such occasions, a balance to set against spectres of anatomy and hallowed halls.

---

50. When I came to Western Canada the population dynamics had changed again. While the commonest cause of an acute abdominal emergency was still acute appendicitis, acute gall bladders now took that second place.

51. John Lawrence, now Lord Oaksey, on his own horse Carrickbeg.

FROM BOSTON TO DUMFRIES

History is all of a piece.
from *A Horseman Riding By*, by R. F. Delderfield

The city of Boston on the eastern seaboard of the United States and the county town of Dumfries in the south-west corner of Scotland both carry honoured and affectionate titles. Boston has long been proclaimed as "The Cradle of Liberty" while Scots refer to Dumfries as "The Queen of the South". Pivotal events in history took place within the confines of the two centres. One was witness in 1306 to Robert the Bruce as he passed the point of no return in his struggle against the English, the other to the incident in 1773 which triggered another war of independence, the Boston Tea Party. Less well known is a nineteenth century medical connection.

William Thomas Green Morton's successful public demonstration of ether anaesthesia in the New World took place in Boston on October 16th 1846, the news subsequently travelling across the Atlantic with passengers on the wooden paddle steamers of the day. How Dumfries came to be the site of the first use of anaesthetic ether for a surgical operation in the Old World has been splendidly told by my friend Tom Baillie.[52] Although there is no suggestion that the operation performed by Dr William Scott in Dumfries on December 19th 1846 made an impact on the acceptance of ether anaesthesia in Europe, that advance clearly getting its impetus from the amputation carried out two days later at Kings College Hospital by the famous London surgeon Robert Liston, the prior case does ensure a place for the old Dumfries and Galloway Royal Infirmary in the annals of anaesthesia. The date of December 19th 1846 is equally marked in those annals as the day London dentist James Robinson administered ether to a patient prior to the painless extraction of a molar tooth. Just over two months later Robinson published a treatise on the inhalation of ether, our speciality's earliest textbook.[53]

---

52. Baillie, T. W. *From Boston to Dumfries*. Dumfries, Dinwoodie, 1966 and Baillie, T. W. *The Dumfries Ether Diary*. Dumfries, Solway, 1996.

53. See Ellis, R. H. *James Robinson on the Inhalation of the Vapour of Ether*. Eastbourne, Bailliere Tindall, 1983.

Although replaced by a new Infirmary almost a century before, the original building had not long been demolished when we came to live and work in Dumfries in the middle of 1965. With exams now out of the way – or so I naïvely thought – I had successfully applied for a position there as Consultant Anaesthetist. We had a number of things to look forward to: my return to Scotland after an absence of seven years; the chance to dust off my golf clubs and get my better half interested in the game; having a fine place for our young family to grow; and most importantly a renewed opportunity of working with the consultant in charge of the local Department of Anaesthesia. Tom Baillie had been the anaesthetist at BMH Tripoli during the first months of my time there and our group from those National Service days had remained a close one. With his first monograph on the ether story now in its final stages, Tom's enthusiasm became infectious. Ideas implanted by a once worshipped teacher began to resurface, and the significance of medical history began to penetrate my consciousness for the first time.

As undergraduate medical students in the early 1950s we had at least heard of some of the great names of medicine, for it had not yet become fashionable to decry the use of eponyms. But if our minds gave any dim recognition to the fact that medicine had a history, the true significance of that history certainly escaped the majority. We walked the same ground as had Joseph Lister, hearing the outlines of his work on antisepsis without seriously questioning its real meaning;[54] we spent our first postgraduate year within almost a stone's throw of the birthplace of the Hunter brothers without developing any desire to learn more of their pioneering work; and we wasted countless other opportunities that were afforded to us. Or I certainly did, assuming, as Leonard Wilson[55] has suggested most young physicians do, that whatever is vital and fascinating in medicine must necessarily be new – new areas of research, new treatments, new cures – and that the medicine of the past had little practical bearing on the present. The gift of a book from my mother at Christmas 1967 also helped to change my outlook.[56] If Tom's tale of ether had given me a glimpse of a fascinating past, it was even more absorbing to find out more about the history of another group of drugs which we used daily in the operating room. I was still some distance away, however, from a full understanding of Delderfield's "history is all of a piece".

---

54. The Glasgow Royal Infirmary dates from 1794. Lister worked in a new Surgical House which opened in 1861. The buildings we knew as students were constructed in the early 1900s.

55. Wilson, L. "Medicine without its history." *J Hist Med Allied Sciences* 1978; **33**, 4: 467-468.

56. Thomas, K. B. *Curare – Its History and Usage*. London, Pitman. 1964.

But this is getting ahead of my story. A living needed to be earned, with lots of patients requiring anaesthesia in a number of differing settings including the Dumfries Infirmary itself, the recently opened Cresswell Maternity Hospital and the nearby Crichton Royal with its huge psychiatric programme. We also travelled to Lochmabon for orthopaedics and occasionally had cases in a not too well equipped private hospital in the centre of Dumfries. Three incidents from those years stand out particularly, as they illustrate how problems in anaesthesia can result from one's own actions or lack of them, from someone else's actions or lack of them and also from vagaries of physiology and pharmacology which are largely out of one's own control.

I learned a lesson the hard way early one morning in Dumfries after being called from sleep to give an anaesthetic to an apparently healthy young man. After a long evening in a pub he had been stabbed in the abdomen and chest by his best friend. By the time I got to the hospital he was lying uncomfortably in a darkened four-bedded ward. While the other men in the room tossed and turned in attempts to regain their rudely interrupted sleep, my patient appeared none too happy, objecting vigorously and retching in response to a nurse's efforts to insert a naso-gastric tube. Noting his totally normal pulse and blood pressure, I asked him the usual standard questions, confirming the fact that he was a healthy and active twenty-two-year-old with no previous illnesses, no medical problems, no previous surgery, on no medications and with no allergies. A run of the mill case? How wrong can one be? As I headed for the operating room I was about to find out.

The patient arrived some ten minutes later with a note from the ward. Repeated attempts at passing the naso-gastric tube had proved unsuccessful. Hazard number one then, stab wounds as yet of unknown extent; hazard number two now added, a stomach full of beer. I gave him an extended period of oxygen and with suction at the ready proceeded with what is referred to as a rapid sequence intravenous induction of anaesthesia, designed to allow immediate intubation and control of the airway. His jaw opened only an inch. I blinked and tried again, but despite complete muscular relaxation the mandible resolutely refused to budge. Moments later the beer began to emerge from his mouth and nose, onto the operating table first and thence to the floor. Any anaesthetist can visualise the subsequent scenario, viewed with increasing alarm by surgeon Bill Seright through the glass-fronted door leading to the adjacent operating room. Thanks to the priceless help of the anaesthetic nurse and an assisting orderly I eventually managed to regain some measure of control, and with the airway unsafely secured by means of a rubber naso-pharyngeal tube we wheeled the operating table through the glass doors to begin the surgery. The beer? With luck most of it had been left behind on the floor of the anaesthetic room.

Hard work might be the best description of the next two and a half hours, hard for the surgeon since with the patient breathing spontaneously I was unable to provide him with any significant muscular relaxation, and hard, physically demanding work for every finger of both of my hands without which it would not have been possible to maintain at least a semblance of an unobstructed airway. Apart from the lack of relaxation, however, the operative side of things went without a hitch, although it proved tedious to establish that the several stab wounds had done no more than cause a number of superficial abrasions to the surface of the bowel. After completion of the abdominal closure, Bill turned his eyes to the wound under the left breast.

'If you want to explore that chest wound, you'll have to do a tracheostomy,' I told him immediately.

The patient's general condition appeared so good, however, in spite of the long struggle with the airway, that we decided that the chest wound could not be a significant one and called a halt for the night – or rather for the early morning. The young chap never turned a hair, developed no post-operative chest problems of any sort and left the hospital well in a little over a week. On a somewhat rueful visit on my part the following morning he complained a bit about a sore neck and throat, readily admitting now to his one major health problem. His mouth had not opened properly since the age of eleven! He was so used to this situation, even to difficulties in chewing solid food, that it had just become a part of normal living. The ward nurse later volunteered that although she had noticed the patient having difficulty in emptying his mouth during the process of retching, because of the poor light in the room she did not think it worthy of comment. If I have some arthritis in the small joints of my fingers these days, I am sure the condition must have begun that night. Don't let anyone ever tell you that anaesthesia is easy. And oh, yes, 'can you open your mouth for me' was a request I never again forgot! With the benefit of hindsight it would have been better to let the patient wake up, have Bill do a tracheostomy and start again from scratch. But managing a difficult airway manually was a challenge which we welcomed in those distant days.

Difficulties of someone else's making? The senior consultant in anaesthesia in Dumfries, the late Bob Keir, was finishing off a day-long list in one operating theatre at the Infirmary and I had reached a similar stage in another. A call for help came from the Cresswell Maternity Hospital where the junior member of our department was apparently in trouble. By the time Bob and I arrived the patient, a totally healthy lady in her twenties, was in obvious respiratory distress. During the next half hour or so we were faced with the successive collapse of both lungs and the development of what is known as acute cardiac tamponade.[57] The cause? A momentary lapse of concentration on the part of the young anaesthetist who failed to notice excessive pressure developing in the anaesthetic circuit. Underwater drains were needed from both sides of the chest cavity, and although this patient did astonishingly well it shows yet again how rapidly things can go wrong in any operating room.

While such a near disaster should never have happened, others can develop just as rapidly from the ups and downs of everyday anaesthesia and though clinical situations may vary widely, similar sorts of stories can readily be equalled from the career of any experienced anaesthetist. Even the doyen of anaesthesia, the late Harold Griffith, the first president of the World Federation of Anesthesiologists and the man who published the first report of the successful use of the muscle relaxant curare, set down a list of personal errors.[58] It is salutary to remember that every single surgical operation and anaesthetic can result in a minor or major complication, even death, no matter how small the risk of the latter may be, and to recall again that the first recorded death from chloroform did not come during any major surgery but rather during the induction of anaesthesia for the removal of an ingrowing toenail. And in case any reader should consider a case from well over a century ago to be irrelevant, I can cite another death from surgery for that very same condition in much more recent times, when a tragic chain of events was triggered off in a Western Canadian hospital by nothing other than totally stupid behaviour on the part of a patient.

These sorts of incidents are not everyday occurrences, of course, but the public should realise that everyday anaesthesia is not simply a question of an intravenous injection followed by uneventful sleep and awakening. Problems occur in all kinds of areas. I have always considered that it was part of the responsibility of our job to shelter patients from the worry of such things. Now I am not so sure. There has been a veritable revolution in the doctor-patient relationship in recent years. While I do not suggest we provide pre-operative homework in the form of anaesthetic textbooks, perhaps it is time to bring a sampling of these risks into the open.

Although much less often precipitated by the newer volatile anaesthetic agents, cardiac arrhythmias (irregularities) can still occur. Many are innocuous, others dangerous if left uncorrected. Sometimes due to pre-existing disease, they can be altered or triggered off in a wide variety of situations, notably in response to the action of drugs and to different kinds of surgical traction. The introduction of an oesphagoscope in one patient of mine in Dumfries sent her heart rate from eighty to over two hundred in an instant, seemingly regular but virtually uncountable in

---

57. An impending complete failure of the action of the heart, in this case due to the leakage of massive amounts of air into the thoracic cavity, perhaps from ruptured bullae although this was never established.

58. See *The Boundless Realm of Anesthesiology. A Collection of the Works of Harold Randall Griffith*. Montreal, Squibb, 1963.

the days before ECG monitoring. Removal of the instrument and the rate returned to eighty once more. Each attempt by ENT surgeon Isobel Bryson to retrieve a fish bone lodged in the gullet produced this identical response;[59] to our joint relief she managed on the fourth or fifth try. Surgical traction on structures as different as the bowel and the muscles of the eyeball can slow the heart dramatically, and drug interactions can occur in many different ways. I recall giving an anaesthetic for an hour-long eye operation, during which the surgeon regularly applied a sterile irrigating solution to prevent the surface of the cornea from drying out. I barely noticed him applying a couple of eye drops from a different looking drop-bottle, but within thirty seconds most definitely noticed the patient's heart rate dropping like a stone, sixty… fifty… forty… thirty-five… While correction of the falling rate was simple, accompanied by very forceful confirmation of the nature of the drops, few lay folk have any idea that drugs can be absorbed almost as fast from mucous membranes as by the intravenous route. I've even seen an elderly man convulsing within seconds of a gross overdose of a local anaesthetic gel given via the urethra.

It would require a book to document the difficulties which can occur with patients' airways, and despite many advances there will always be problems lurking in this area. Most can be anticipated, some cannot. I am a reluctant shopper at the best of times, so I often keep myself occupied during unavoidable excursions by unobtrusively observing the diversity of the passing crowd: a grossly obese individual, a markedly receding chin or a broad Mongolian jaw; all are red lights for the wary anaesthetist, especially in the third of such scenarios if accompanied by flashes of gold suggestive of extensive dental work.

Unexpected happenings occur in all areas of life, however, and anaesthesia was only marginally involved in the biggest surprise of my life. Just a few months after my unexpected encounter with the young man with the fixed jaw, I waited anxiously by the side of a telephone. Betty had gone into hospital the day before, due to undergo a Caesarean section the following day for the delivery of our third child. Fathers only rarely attended normal deliveries in those days and they were never present in the operating room. I grabbed the phone as soon as it rang, a close friend by my side becoming instantly concerned by my sudden stunned silence. The instant doubling in size of one's family takes a bit of getting used to. In retrospect the only person not totally taken aback by the news of the unexpected arrival of twins was the mother of the babies, for Betty – a midwife herself – had always insisted she could feel a head under her ribs as well as the one felt down in her pelvis. Ultrasound examinations were still in their infancy.

Enlarging families necessitate a number of things; assorted additional outfits, many donated on this occasion by equally surprised friends; a twin pram, which in

---

59. Paroxysmal atrial tachycardia, though we never had any evidence to prove it.

the event our third daughter steadfastly refused to share equably with her brother; and a new and larger car. And in the course of time thoughts of the challenge of a new job in a new country. Why did we make the move to Canada? It wasn't an easy decision, particularly with the prospect of having to satisfy yet another set of examiners. Good friends would be left behind, including a surgeon with whom I very greatly enjoyed working and a valued golfing partner. Our living conditions, even the surrounding culture would be vastly different, the winters longer and colder. I carried the resignation letter in my pocket for several days before summoning up enough courage to post it.

CONTRAST AND CHANGE

Medicine has a changing and unchanging face, and it is
as necessary to learn the meaning of the first as it is to
cherish the second.
Sir F. M. R. Walshe

'Why did we have to come to Canada?' The question came from our eldest daughter. I'm not sure if I came up with a very convincing answer. It was very hot. An airline strike had greatly extended our flight from London and our scattered belongings were now strewn across an airless room in a slightly seedy looking Edmonton motel, Betty was doing her best to comfort the exceedingly fractious twins. However encouraging I had found the familiar blossoms on many of the city's trees as we drove in from the airport, they would hardly have provided much solace to a child of six. Having grown up in a house which stood in the shade of a huge rowan tree and spent many wonderful holidays in another named "Rowanbrae", I regarded all rowans as Scottish born and bred. I soon discovered that this name meant as little to most Edmontonians as that of its close botanical cousin[60] did to me. Nor could we offer our children the prospect of a visit to the amusement and adventure areas of the largest shopping mall in the world, for West Edmonton Mall had not yet advanced beyond the drawing board stage.

Edmonton offered much more than the big Mall, however, both then and now, and although it took around three months for our feeling of homesickness to disappear, a Christmas holiday in Britain eighteen months later confirmed the correctness of the decision. Despite balmy temperatures and green fields we couldn't wait to get back to frozen Alberta! Having lived almost all of his adult life in Kenya it remained a puzzle to my brother Graham that anyone could voluntarily accept life at less than zero on the Fahrenheit scale, even for part of a year, and he refused to even contemplate the minus fifty figure which we recorded outside our house on one

---

60. The North American Mountain Ash.

occasion. I don't think he ever believed our insistence that we had felt much colder in the damp climate of the UK.

More than four decades have passed since our move. Trying to pick out a few of the highlights is not an easy task, but two words stand out – *contrast* and *change*. They certainly applied to our surroundings. In trading the hills of Dumfries and Galloway for the prairies of Alberta we had made exchanges other than those of climate: from a known school system for our children to a totally new one; from the roadside sight of the cricket field to that of the baseball diamond; from sports where hitting an opponent off the ball is penalised to those in which this constitutes an integral part of the game; from curious licensing laws to even more curious and restrictive ones; from unrestricted jay walking to the prospect of a fine for such activity; and from the undulating green grass of Epsom and Sandown to what seemed to me the uninspiring dirt race tracks of North America. We quickly adjusted to most of these changes, however, and with our growing family beginning to settle into school and into a diversity of new activities began to put down some roots.

My new job came with a number of advantages. The chance, in the event one that lasted for more than twenty years, of working with a now greatly missed friend and colleague, the late Ian St Clair, who understood respiratory physiology better than any other anaesthetist I have ever known; the major teaching commitment of the Edmonton General; the sense of family which clearly emanated from its medical staff, built around the tradition of their annual Mousseau Lectureship; and yet another link with Tripoli, as Bill and Ruth Liston had moved to Edmonton more than a decade before.

The range of surgery performed in the General's ten operating rooms offered a significant widening to my anaesthetic horizons and in time there were other new options, particularly the splendid library of the University of Alberta where I could begin to indulge my increasing interest in medical history. That library helped, too, in my preparation for the Canadian Certification in Anaesthesia a few months after our arrival, as did Betty's enormous support at this time, keeping our four young children out of the way while I bashed the books once more. My luck in examination halls still held. I could hardly believe my eyes when I looked at the first question – anaesthesia for a patient with a phaeochromocytoma. Many hours had gone into the paper I had published on this subject while in Dumfries and what must have been close to an error-free answer left lots of time to tackle the remaining topics. I nearly came unstuck in the oral, however, blurting out a couple of statements I immediately wanted to retract, as examinees are often wont to do. A second unscheduled oral was added on as a result, with two new examiners. I made the grade with them, fortunately, though nearly not with Betty who had expected to hear from me much, much earlier that long afternoon.

Contrast and *change* remain the key words from the years that followed, with the changing and unchanging faces of medicine clearly illustrated in terms of professional attitudes, advances in techniques and treatment, teaching and training, and even in newer ways of moving patients through the hospital system. Some may regard the changing face as being simply another expression for progress, which the dictionary defines as "to advance or develop especially to a better state". But while we continue to advance it may not always be for the better.

Although given a decided push by the politicians and by society as a whole, medicine took a new road in these decades, turning away from its professional past and beginning to look much like any other business. I agree entirely with my friend Kenneth Brown's comment that with increasing emphasis on monetary value there has been a sea change in the attitude of doctors, many of whom have become much harder, more interested in themselves and less concerned about their patients. "Concerned" may not be the best choice of word, but certainly less involved. Who now remembers, for example, that obstetricians once cancelled holidays to remain in town for potentially difficult labours, or that rather than routinely transferring care to someone else on call a surgeon would abandon weekend plans when a patient developed significant post-operative complications? How many of today's physicians would happily accept the professional courtesy we offered in Kenya – no charge for treating any family member of a doctor, dentist or minister of religion, in or out of hospital, nor for similarly taking care of any nursing colleague? Advertising by physicians, permitted nowadays by the professional licensing bodies in a steadily increasing manner, is another obvious symptom of this change.

Changes in practice occurred in all areas, and anaesthesia was no exception. Our machines began to take on a different look. Old and inefficient glass vaporising bottles disappeared, replaced by gleaming temperature compensated models with names appropriate for the agent they contained;[61] cyclopropane and ether were banned because of the risk of explosion; ventilators increasingly became direct attachments to anaesthetic machines, no longer free standing as they had been in the past; pulse monitors and nerve stimulators came into general use, followed by heart monitors and pulse oximeters;[62] and as screens displayed the ongoing activity of our patients' hearts the old and friendly image of the Boyle's machine faded into memory. We now found a new worry, concerns being raised about the effects of residual anaesthetic gases and vapours on operating room staff. A raised incidence

---

61. Fluotec for fluothane (halothane) and Pentec for penthrane. These agents are no longer used.

62. Technology continues to advance, with current and future possibilities almost intimidating to those of us who trained in the fifties and sixties, and with computerisation of anaesthetic records a far cry from days when we simply entered "GA. Pentothal, Gas, Oxygen and Fluothane" on a patient's chart!

of miscarriages among operating staff and an effect on the sex of children of male anaesthetists were both suggested, with figures in the latter case indicating a higher than expected number of girls. We made a quick tally of our own Department. Seven male staff members, seventeen girls and six boys! We looked at each other, didn't pass the figures on, concentrating instead on ways of exhausting the contaminated air from the machines and operating rooms. Thinking back to the times when I had often given open ether, when we simply put gowns over our outside clothes on entering an operating room, I remember Betty often complaining that I stank of the agent. 'Just from my clothes,' I would reply. But it wasn't from my clothes. I had been inhaling ether vapour from around the mask. I even have to admit to developing a bit of a liking for the smell!

If the years brought about change, the individuality of patients provided much of the contrast. How about a centenarian, a three-hour-old baby and a patient that never was? The first of these, her strong Scottish accent giving us an immediate bond, had slipped and sustained a fractured femur whilst helping her seventy-nine year old daughter to change a mattress. She proved an entirely straightforward case, the easiest anaesthetic imaginable, being discharged home from the Edmonton General in excellent shape some ten days later. The young infant was another matter altogether, one of the most difficult and stressful cases of my anaesthetic career, one which illustrates yet again how one can never take anything for granted in our less than perfect world.

I was working away from the General at this time. Having anaesthetised the mother for a Caesarean delivery shortly after midnight I knew that we would almost certainly be called back to the operating room, since the major developmental deformity had been obvious at birth, a defect in the baby's abdominal wall allowing the protrusion of loops of bowel. As expected, the paediatric surgeon opted for an immediate primary closure.

Describing the situation in its mildest terms, with considerable intra-abdominal pressure required to return the bowel to its proper place, adequate ventilation of the lungs became a major challenge. With the very able help of the senior anaesthetic resident, Dave Hunt, however, we managed to survive a number of crises, finishing the case with the infant in what would nowadays be termed critical but stable condition. Unfortunately we were not yet out of the woods. The paediatric intensive care unit was several floors and a few hundred yards distant from the main operating suite. Few hospital elevators have enough space for a transporting an incubator, a nurse and three doctors, with one of the latter ventilating a critically ill baby by hand. Though this night was no exception, space proved to be the least of our problems. One might reasonably expect that oxygen cylinders on an incubator would have been checked prior to its dispatch from a neonatal ICU. This had not been done that night and that we then failed to double check compounded the error. Never take anything for granted, even more so at five or six in the morning. Three floors up, struggling to emerge from the elevator, the incubator's oxygen ran out.

A couple of minutes can seem like an eternity, especially in a dark and eerily silent hospital corridor, the only sound that of my rapid puffing down the endotracheal tube, waiting for Dave as he charged back down several flights of stairs to grab a new cylinder from the main OR, then back up again to attach and turn it on. The infant came through this added stress without harm; I doubt if any member of the attending team has forgotten it. The obvious lesson – mistakes are most likely to occur, have always been most likely to occur, when people are tired. I know of a case during a very extended surgical procedure where a tight limb tourniquet lay forgotten under the surgical drapes for an unforgivable length of time. The reason – a change of nursing shift at seven am and a team of surgeons already fatigued from an entire evening and night of work. I also remember an occasion during my residency days at Whipps Cross when Ken Slack and I both failed to realise at five am that whilst supervising my administration of an anaesthetic to an extremely sick patient he had rested his elbow on the oxygen bypass of the anaesthetic machine. We recognised the fact that we had gone through a cylinder of oxygen extremely quickly, but not the reason why. In that particular case the omission may actually have helped the patient!

The patient who never was? He came my way, or rather did not come my way, one Saturday morning in 1984. Pope John Paul II was visiting Edmonton, due to say Mass before a huge crowd at the Namao airbase in the north of the city. Well known as an avid hill-walker whenever a rare free few hours arose, the Pope had indicated his wish to take a break from the formal programme. With the Rocky Mountains only a short distance away by air, they became first choice for a projected contemplative hike. Elaborate security and medical coverage followed his every move, particularly in the aftermath of the previous attempt on his life. Now such attention had to be extended to include the Jasper region. Although local surgeons indicated their willingness to be on standby, other family physicians were less than happy at the prospect, however remote, of any medical or anaesthetic responsibility for such a patient. Dr Fred MacDonald was in charge of the medical arrangements for the Papal visit, with internist Bob Lefebvre co-ordinating the Jasper team, and they asked me if I would be willing to join in. After putting together a suitable selection of portable emergency equipment and drugs, Bob and I headed for the Namao airport just before dawn, boarding a helicopter belonging to the provincial government as the crowds were beginning to gather for the Mass.

I had never flown in such an aircraft before, nor been used to such luxurious seating, and the flight proved quite an experience. Even as we started, however, the possibility of its being aborted loomed large, for the weather forecast for the Jasper area became somewhat ominous. Definitely on... possibly off... the outlook kept changing as we listened in to both ends of the cockpit conversation. In the event we had almost arrived at the Hinton airport when advisors called the whole trip off. Anaesthetist-in-waiting for John Paul II for a few hours, I had to content myself with that thought. There is a postscript, too, for the Pope went instead by car to nearby Elk Island Park, where for a few anxious moments he and a childhood friend became separated from their security guards. Fred has told the full story of that Saturday, and of the sudden radio message – 'We've lost the Pope!'[63] Just another day on call for all concerned, though perhaps a little out of the ordinary on this occasion.

If the negative side of progress is represented by increasing bureaucracy and by an allied change in professional attitudes, the positive side is represented by the continuing improvements in clinical medicine. Choose any description you like – the passing of light years, chalk from cheese, day from night, science from art – they all apply. *Staggering* might be another adjective to apply to the changes and advances since the start of my anaesthetic training in 1957. Let's take a look at a few of them.

We have gone from a time when almost every surgical patient came from an in-patient bed to a time when the majority are admitted on the morning of surgery, and from the era when deeply unconscious patients were transferred directly from the operating table to their beds in the surgical ward to the modern concept of recovery within the confines of the operating suite. The staff of these recovery units would be astonished to learn of a superstition that patients must not be allowed to return to their own beds "feet first" – for that might be an omen of a later departure from bed and hospital in similar fashion. I once witnessed an unconscious patient vomiting on a stretcher whilst in transit from the operating room, the nurse walking backwards at the head end of the stretcher being more involved with the negotiation of a narrow corridor than with looking at her patient. Only then did I finally manage to have this policy altered.

Can today's ICU nurses possibly imagine what it was like to treat a crushed chest injury, with a floating sternum and multiple rib fractures, in a side room off a busy surgical ward without the benefit of any monitoring other than the recording of vital signs? Yet that is what we had to do in Dumfries in the mid-1960s. Even more surprising, perhaps, is the fact that such management worked. Look back even further to the 1920s and 1930s when a critically injured patient might be treated in a small cottage hospital with a consultant from the big city calling in to see him once a day. Intensive care has definitely moved on! That anaesthetists in many parts of the

---

63. MacDonald, G. F. in Blumer, L. C. *Sharing The Journey.* Edmonton, Tree Frog Press, 1999, pp. 76-78.

world played a leading role in the development of this field, as also in coronary care, is still not fully recognised.

Contrast and change? How about training in anaesthesia? Although revolution-ised in almost every way, as has already been noted in relation to undergraduate students, I came across more than one senior resident in the 1970s and 1980s who had quite clearly been left in sole charge of anaesthetised patients on the rarest of occasions. As they were supposed to be almost ready for solo practice this was surely not much better than our being thrown in at the deep end. Teaching also depends on current thinking. We gave oxygen prior to the induction of anaesthesia only in the sickest of patients or for emergency cases. Now virtually everyone is pre-oxygenated. We were taught to only intubate the trachea in the presence of a specific indication; our immediate successors were taught the very reverse – intubate all anaesthetised patients unless there is a reason not to! Though this latter policy took a new direc-tion in the 1980s following the introduction of the laryngeal mask airway (LMA), newcomers to the speciality might be surprised to learn that even in the matter of the maintenance of a clear airway, the most vital element of a good anaesthetic, everything changes yet nothing changes, for despite very significant differences in purpose, design and material, the LMA can be described as a distant cousin of an airway developed in Regina more than seventy years ago.[64] And while we relied on a simple tray for difficult intubations, portable trolleys now carry sophisticated video equipment and endoscopes. Night from day, but the challenge remains.

Changing and unchanging – how many other examples do you want? How about anaesthesia for Caesarean section? At Bellshill in Lanarkshire in 1953 when I was an intern at nearby Hairmyres Hospital every single patient requiring a section received a spinal anaesthetic, obstetrician Bob Tennant getting excellent results with both mothers and babies. By the late 1950s when I took my early obstetric and anaesthetic training at Robroyston and Paisley, virtually all were under general anaesthesia, for by then spinals in Britain had fallen under a major cloud. Generals remained the order of the day until the resurgence of interest in epidural anaesthesia under the influence of Philip Bromage and others. Soon these epidurals became all the rage on both sides of the Atlantic, with fewer and fewer patients asleep for their operative deliveries, this despite the fact that even in the best of hands the analgesia could occasionally be less than perfect, and certainly less intense than that obtained with a spinal. Now general anaesthesia is used only rarely for Caesareans and unless an epidural catheter is already in place spinal anaesthesia has regained its old popularity as the method of choice.[65] Regional anaesthesia, more correctly termed regional analgesia, has also

---

64. Leech, B. C. "The pharyngeal bulb gasway." *Anesth Analg* 1937; **16**: 22-25.

65. A combination of spinal and epidural anaesthesia can also be employed.

undergone a resurgence, with ultrasound monitors and other methods ensuring better blockage of individual nerves or groups of nerves. The understanding of the anatomy behind such blocks, of course, is nothing new. Labat's classic treatise on regional anaesthesia,[66] a copy of which was presented to me when I left Dumfries, was first published in 1922. And if the wheel has turned full circle for spinals these past fifty years, replacement of almost everything else provides the newer face to complement the old. In the light of the recent death of a well-known celebrity, look for propofol to supplant pentothal in future murder mysteries!

One thing does not change. Whatever else may be said of it the job of an anaesthetist is never lacking in variety, for a routine day or night can turn in a moment to the management of a horrendous injury, as two cases from the 1980s illustrate. In the first an uneventful emergency list was interrupted near midnight by a call to Emergency to see the victim of a car accident, a young girl in her early twenties. A guard rail had come through the windshield of her car in a high speed crash, shattering her face. When the plastic surgeon and I first saw her in the casualty department the immediate necessity was for control and protection of the airway. On opening her mouth, the whole lower jaw and neck simply fell away, leaving the laryngeal opening in direct view through a mess of damaged tissues and blood. With reassurance taking the place of any form of sedation until the airway was secured, intubation proved surprisingly simple. The day staff had come on duty by the time the facial repair had been completed. A gratifying success, I suppose, though only the future could tell what the final psychological and cosmetic result might be, as uncertain an outcome as that of another case which rudely interrupted a Saturday afternoon a year or so later.

A six-year-old girl had wandered away from her parents at a nearby major air show. Following the unexpected crash of a small plane, a cart-wheeling wing struck her in the midriff, coming close to severing the lower half of her body, inflicting probably the worst set of non-fatal injuries that I had ever seen, including major muscle damage and disruption of bowel, blood vessels and nerves. Many, many hours of painstaking reconstruction followed, a general and plastic surgeon working in tandem, with litres of blood and other intravenous fluids being required. A decade earlier this young child would not have survived. The combination of modern invasive monitoring and newer techniques of anaesthesia made all the difference. If members of the public were more aware of such scenes their responses to surveys would quickly change!

Anaesthetists play a vital part today in the care of patients who survive from conditions far graver than we could ever have imagined in the past. If one takes a

---

66. Labat, G. *Regional Anesthesia.* Philadelphia, Saunders (editions were published in 1922, 1928 and 1967).

close look at those who enter today's operating rooms and compares them to their parents or grandparents who made similar journeys forty and more years ago, the contrast is quite extraordinary, perhaps the single biggest change during the span of my own career. Looking at the workload of an individual anaesthetist on any given day in the year 2010, from thirty percent to as high as fifty, even to a hundred percent of the cases on some days, would have been considered quite unfit for any anaesthesia or surgery in the late 1950s. Although the care available in post-operative recovery rooms in this transformation must be fully acknowledged, continuing on into intensive care units, if anyone wonders what an anaesthetist does for a living I can tell you that he or she has to deal today with the management of increasingly sicker and sicker patients – and always on a one-to-one basis. While we may have failed to cultivate personal relationships with our patients, anaesthetists serve the members of the public better and more fully than they know.

Can one make any sense from all these contrasts and changes? I would suggest that this is only possible in the context of history, by following the paths of a few of the many individuals involved and by relating their innovative efforts to the social context of their times. Although only limited aspects of many, many fascinating tales can be covered in a personal account such as this, a brief review may help to bring the little-known world of anaesthesia into clearer focus. While I could be accused of putting the cart before the horse in starting in the following way, this is where my interest in medical history began.

Left: *RB Cunninghame Graham (1920s)*
Below: *Bringing back a faller - Dr John Humble at Hurst Park (1930s)*

Top Left: *Poppa Bobbin - Glasgow University Charities Day (1951) L to R: Jim Aitken, Roy Humble, Iain Glen, Alistair Riddell and Ronald Howie*
Top Right: *Learning to be soldiers - 2nd Lieuts Humble and Styles (1954)*
Above: *The Old Austin gave us some problems (1952)*

Top: *2 Field Ambulance at Suez base camp (1955)*
Above: *2 Field Ambulance heading for a desert exercise (1955)*
Left: *Medical staff, 2 Field Engineers Regt., Tripoli (1955)*

Left: *Looking out towards a vast blue sea. The Theatre, Leptis Magna (1955-56)*
Below: *Breaking all the rules. British Military Hospital, Tripoli (1955)*

Left: *In the footsteps of Livingstone. Victoria Falls (1958)*
Below: *Nakuru township and Lake Nakuru from the golf course (1960)*
Bottom: *Ortum Mission Hospital, Suk Valley, Kenya (1960) - note tarpaulin covers for outdoor TB beds*

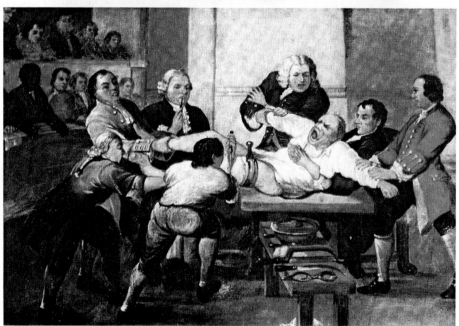

Top: *Richard Gill watching the preparation of curare. Ecuador (1938)*
Above: *Before the advent of modern anaesthesia, a scene at the old St Thomas's Hospital in Southwark (late eighteenth century)*

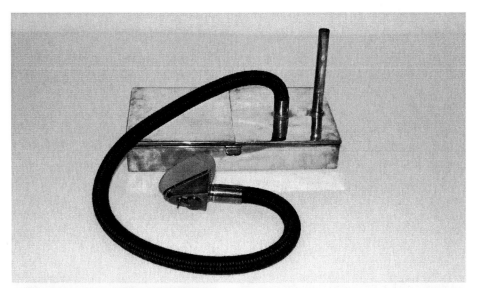

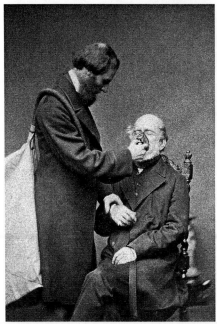

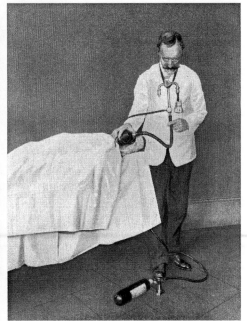

Top: *Replica of Snow Ether inhaler (1847)*
Above Left: *Joseph Clover's method of administering chloroform in air from a pre-filled bag (1862)*
Above Right: *Vernon Harcourt chloroform inhaler in use with foot control for added oxygen (from Buxton DW.* Anaesthetics. *London, Lewis, 1920)*

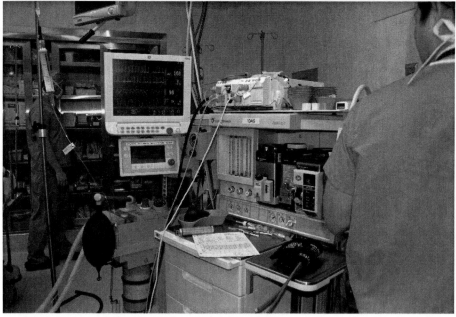

Top: *Mid twentieth century Boyle's machine used by Dr Tom Baillie and the author in Dumfries in the 1960s. L to R: Dr Hugh Brewster, Dr Roy Humble, Prof. Wm. Bowman and Dr Tom Baillie (Speakers at Dumfries meeting 1996 - see page 131)*
Above: *Anaesthetic equipment in use in the early twenty first century*

PART TWO
<u>LOOKING BACK</u>

CONNECTIONS
THE FLYING DEATH

If you poison us, do we not die?
Shakespeare

In his fine presentation of the story of curare,[1] Bryn Thomas wrote of a man called Richard Gill that he "provided the main link between the jungle and the anaesthetist". Few lay people recognise that the necessity for such a link should ever have existed, let alone its full significance. That reference to Gill led me on a thirty-year pilgrimage to some widely scattered places: to the Arthur E. Guedel Library in San Francisco to review all of his papers and memorabilia; to Stanford University and Palo Alto to visit and talk with Bill Neff, one of the early workers with curare who had known Gill personally; to Washington, DC, where after a significant battle with the freeway traffic my eldest daughter and I were given a fine afternoon tea by Gill's long-time secretary, Violet Ohlsen, who gave us much background information; to the University of Iowa to present the 1984 Louis W. Harding Lecture; to Walton Hall in the West Riding of Yorkshire to visit the old home of an eccentric conservationist; and finally back full circle to Dumfries for a historic meeting to celebrate the sesquicentennial of the first administration of anaesthetic ether for a surgical operation in the Old World. To put these travels into the context of Gill's work, however, I have to begin by looking much further back.

Most patients are unaware of the fact that a large percentage of the anaesthetics given in our modern era include the administration of one or more of a group of drugs which are the successors of "the flying death", the collective early name for the arrow poisons of South America. To have any real understanding of modern anaesthesia they must start in the sixteenth century with the dreams of the Conquistadors and their search for the fabled City of Gold, realising at the outset that the story of the harnessing of these naturally occurring agents is no different from any other chapter in medical history.

During a landmark 1978 television series, *Connections*, James Burke stressed the fact that no one individual has ever been responsible for any major scientific

---

1.   Thomas, K. B. *Curare – Its History and Usage*. London, Pitman, 1964.

advance. Each move forward comes from a variety of connections, often unrelated but always influenced by the social climate of the times in which they occur. Consisting as it does of a complicated jigsaw puzzle put together over a span of four centuries by an intriguingly diverse cast of characters, the curare story is no different. Each individual solves one piece of the puzzle or provides a link with the next person to come upon the stage. Many are well ahead of their contemporaries, some are far-sighted thinkers, others mainly doers. Some are acknowledged by their peers and by history, others only given a reputation after death, while an unfortunate few receive little or no mention in the pages of time.

Although its origins go even further back, the modern history of the South American arrow poison begins in 1555. Not expecting much in the way of opposition in view of their superiority in weapons and with a presumption of much greater intelligence, the would-be conquerors of the New World had their visions of El Dorado turn into something of a nightmare, as Pieter Martyr reported to the Spanish Court. Describing how one party of sailors had been ambushed by a band of naked warriors after landing in search of a supply of fresh water, he wrote:

> ...*So fiercely assayling oure men with theire venomous arrowes that they slewe of them fortie and seven... for that poyson is of such force, that albeit the wounds were not great, yet they dyed thereof immediately.*[2]

Rather than the actual nature of the arrow poison, the search for a possible antidote pre-occupied the minds of all the early explorers, with salt, sea water, urine, tobacco, garlic and other vegetables all receiving mention. Sir Walter Raleigh summed it up in 1596:

> *There was nothing whereof I was more curious than to find out the true remedies of these poisoned arrows, for besides the mortalitie of the wound they make, the partie shotte endureth the most unsufferable torment in the world, and abideth a most ugly and lamentable death.*[3]

The name *ourari*, referring to one of several poisonous herbs, first appears in English the same year in the writings of Raleigh's lieutenant, Lawrence Keymis. Then something of a veil descends, the colonial aspirations of Spain and Portugal and the greed for gold combining to close down the South American continent to scientific

---

2.   Thomas, K. B. *ibid.*, p. 14.

3.   Thomas, K. B. ibid., p. 19.

explorers for most of the seventeenth century. It was not until 1735 that the first of a new generation of travellers arrived in Ecuador, sent from Paris primarily for navigational purposes to compare measurements from the other side of the world.

Charles Marie de la Condamine spent ten years in South America, bringing back a great deal more than mere measurements, including the first samples of the continent's platinum. He also gave this description of the use of the poison:

> ...*The Yameos (an Indian tribe in the foothills of the Andes) propel by their breath small arrows of wood to a distance of many paces, and rarely miss their target. ...They cover the points of the arrows with a poison so active that, when it is fresh, it will kill in less than a minute any animal whose blood it has entered...*[4]

Although rather spoiling things by insisting that sugar was a dependable antidote, an effect he was unable to demonstrate in experiments with chickens on his return to Europe, de la Condamine nevertheless brought the flying death out of the realm of the lurid tales of travellers and into the arena of scientific investigation. He also suggested that of more than thirty ingredients used by another tribe the most important appeared to come from several varieties of the jungle bush ropes, or lianas, which covered the gigantic trees of the region. Thirty years later Edward Bancroft pointed out that the poison varied according to the ingredients used by different tribes and confirmed de La Condamine's suggestion that the active ingredient came from the lianas. Bancroft also described how the ingredients were slowly evaporated over a fire to the consistency of tar, into which, after cooling, the tips of the arrows were dipped.

In May 1800, during their remarkable journey of scientific exploration to the New World, Alexander von Humboldt and Aimé Bonpland reached what was almost the end of the known world, Esmeralda, in the remotest part of Venezuela, witnessing and accurately recording the preparation of curare by the Indian witch doctors. von Humboldt describes how the natives were all drunk, celebrating their return from an expedition to collect the ingredients of the poison, including the lianas of the region. One elder was less drunk than the others:

> ...*this old Indian was known throughout the mission by the name of the poison master (the Amo del curare). He had that self sufficient air and tone of pedantry... I know, he said, that the whites have the secret of making soap, and manufacturing that black powder which has the defect of making noise when used in killing animals.*

4.   Thomas, K. B. *ibid.*, p. 25.

The woorari which we prepare from father to son is superior to anything you can make beyond the sea. It is the juice of a herb which kills instantly, without anyone knowing whence the stroke comes.[5]

Von Humboldt discovered through his own experiments that the poison could be tasted without harm, that it had to be absorbed into the blood and that it had no direct effect on the nerves. He was the first to bring back a significant quantity of curare to the Old World, some of which remained available for the use of later investigators. As he pondered on the puzzle of the flying death, von Humboldt made a forecast that:

...a fine chemical and physiological investigation remains to be accomplished... when the ingredients can be obtained, without being confounded together from the places where they are prepared.[6]

Sir Benjamin Collins Brodie, one of the leading English surgeons of the nineteenth century, carried out a number of experiments early in his career on guinea pigs and cats in which he proved that the practical antidote to the poison was the continuance of artificial respiration for the duration of its action. He also carried this work further in association with a quite remarkable individual.

The inhabitants of Walton, in the West Riding of Yorkshire, classed their local squire as decidedly eccentric. They had heard that he slept on bare wooden boards, with a wooden block for a pillow, and that he routinely climbed and remained in trees for periods of hours. As if that wasn't enough, having surrounded his property with a six-foot-high stone wall he proceeded to encourage visits from the inmates of the local lunatic asylum. His house was known to be full of stuffed animals and even reputedly a human-like head, while many villagers reported that he paid sixpence for every live hedgehog brought to him. He also seemed to be constantly at war with the factory owners who were bringing much-needed employment to the area. Strange behaviour, indeed!

All the early biographers of Charles Waterton, the Squire of Walton Hall, focused on his eccentricities, dwelling on such escapades as his riding on the back of a large alligator and of capturing a live ten-foot boa constrictor by the expedient

---

5. Von Humboldt, A. *Personal Narrative of Travels to the Equinoctial Regions of America*, vol. 2, New York, Blom, 1971 (first published in 1814-25 as *Relation historique du voyage aux regions équinoxiales du nouveau continent*), p. 439.

6. Von Humboldt, A. *ibid.*, p. 445.

of punching it on its nose, having first caught hold of its tail, hustling it then into a bag before it could recover from the shock! Yet although his life story has been likened to one that might have been invented by Edgar Allan Poe, Charles Waterton was undoubtedly a visionary, one of the earliest conservationists. Gerald Durrell has written of him:

> *It was Waterton who warned that if we did not mend our ways and respect the world we live in and not ravage it, we would go to hell in a handcart.*[7]

Speaking out against the indiscriminate shooting of wildlife, Waterton recognised the connection between the pollution of the Industrial Revolution and the disappearance of certain species, warning also of the consequences of destruction of the rain forest. He encouraged psychiatric patients to view birds through his telescopes, which nowadays would be deemed an entirely appropriate form of occupational therapy, and turned his three-hundred-acre estate into perhaps the earliest bird and animal sanctuary. One wonders what he might think to see his home serving as a *Best Western*, with many of these same acres now used as a golf course. Apart from the modern addition to the rear of the building, however, Walton Hall remains much as it did in his own day, accessible to visitors across the same short stretch of water and with the family crest and motto still plainly visible above the front door.

Waterton's family owned property in British Guiana (known today as Guyana). He travelled widely along the Esquibido River, rarely in the company of any other European, describing these travels in his classic *Wanderings in South America*.[8] Among the earliest of the visitors from the Old World to view the preparation of curare, he conducted animal experiments with his own samples, correctly deducing that the quantity of poison required to kill an animal was proportionate to its size. He later supplied the sample for the famous experiment carried out in London in 1814 by Collins Brodie and the veterinarian William Sewell. Waterton described this operation as follows:

> *...A she-ass received the wourali poison in the shoulder, and apparently died in ten minutes. An incision was then made in its windpipe, and through it the lungs were inflated for two hours with a pair of bellows. Suspended animation returned. The ass held up its*

---

7.   Durrell, G. Foreword to Blackburn, J. *Charles Waterton – Traveller and Conservationist*. London, The Bodley Head, 1989.

8.   Waterton, C. *Wanderings in South America*. London, Macmillan, 1879. (The first edition was published in 1825.)

head, and looked around; but the inflating being discontinued, she
sank once more in apparent death. The artificial respiration was
immediately recommenced, and continued without intermission for
a further two hours. This saved the ass from final dissolution; she
rose up and walked about, and seemed neither in agitation or pain.[9]

To reflect the significance of the occasion, the early name of the poison was turned into an affectionate name for the animal, "Wouralia". Waterton dreamt of success in other ways, too, making it known that he would bring supplies of the poison anywhere in England to a victim of rabies in the hope of being able to use it to relieve the muscular spasms of the then always fatal disease. Although anxious to try out his knowledge in such a case, he insisted that if this treatment should prove successful the full credit should belong to his friend Sewell. Their joint hopes were never realised and although Waterton's unique contribution to the curare story, and indeed to the field of conservation, has slipped into comparative obscurity, his surname is familiar to every visitor to a western Canadian national park.[10]

By the time the great French physiologist Claude Bernard came on the scene, two lianas had been identified as principal sources of the poison, from the genus *Strychnos* mainly in the eastern regions and *Chondodendron* to the west. Some of these bush ropes could rise to a great height, while others carried fruit the size of a large apple, thus confirming the basis for the early explorers' stories of venomous apples. Despite such identification, however, there was still widespread confusion on the botanical problem since different tribes used multiple combinations of plants, many of which contained other alkaloids with a mild curare-like effect.

In a classically simple experiment, described in a collection of lectures published in 1857[11] and backed up by much other work on isolated nerve and muscle preparations, Bernard cut off the circulation to one lower limb of a frog, exposing and isolating the sciatic nerve at the same time. Since an intravenous injection of curare paralysed the animal, with the exception of the ligatured limb, while the muscle on the paralysed side continued to respond to direct galvanic stimulation, as did the excluded sciatic nerve, he postulated that the drug must act by somehow disrupting the connection between nerve and muscle. He thus foreshadowed the discovery of

9. Thomas, K. B. *Curare – Its History and Usage*. London, Pitman, 1964, p. 34.

10. Maltby, J. R. "Charles Waterton (1782-1865): curare and a Canadian national park." *Canadian Anaesthetists' Society Journal* 1982; **29**: 195-202.

11. Bernard, C. *Leçons sur les effets des substances toxiques et médicamenteuses*. Paris, 1857, p. 238 et seq.

the neuro-muscular junction, the structure of which became visible a century later under the electron microscope.

Intermittent progress continued on both pharmacological and physiological fronts in the decades following Bernard's work, moving towards the full understanding of the chemical nature of neuromuscular transmission. It was now recognised that curare blocked that transmission and that its action could be antagonised by the anti-cholinesterase drugs. Although numerous people experimented with the limited quantities which were available, they were always hampered by the same stumbling block, the unpredictability of action between different samples.

The first known experiments related to anaesthesia occurred as far back as 1912 when a little known German doctor Arthur Läwen deliberately used his small supply of curare to relax the abdominal muscles of small animals anaesthetised with ether. Although he also used diluted solutions in humans in combination with narcosis and local anaesthesia and reported that the relaxant effect on the closure of abdominal incisions could be greatly enhanced, he ran up against the same problem:

> ...the effects were not predictable or controllable... and there is not sufficient curare available.[12]

In the early 1930s Ranyard West in Britain used dilute intravenous solutions of curare in the treatment of spastic paralysis, but like Burman and other workers in the States reluctantly came to the conclusion that because of its unpredictability the drug offered little hope of being safely employed in medicine. He left a fine summary of the trials and tribulations of this early work in a paper published when he was well into his retirement years.[13] Despite significant misconceptions particularly in terms of classification, which continued to refer to specimens according to the type of container in which they had been delivered from the jungle,[14] progress continued in the laboratory, and in 1935 Harold King isolated the active principle in a museum specimen of the poison, naming the pure alkaloid *d-tubocurarine*. Although the nature and action of curare was now understood and an alkaloid from one of many different samples positively identified, without the making of one more connection the curare story would have remained bogged down until well after the Second World War. This connection came as the result of the enterprise and determination of one man and his wife.

---

12. Faulconer, A. and Keys, T. E. *Foundations of Anesthesiology*, vol. 2, Springfield, Il., Thomas, 1965, p. 1184.

13. West, R. "An Excursion into Pharmacology: Curare in Medicine." *Medical History* 1984; **28**: 391-405.

14. Termed as a result *pot curare*, *tube curare* or *calabash curare*.

A GREAT DREAM

*To make a great dream come true, the first requirement is
a capacity to dream; the second is persistence – a faith in
that dream.*
Hans Selye

Born in Washington, DC, Richard Gill had a peripatetic early career. Never fully satisfied with any one particular occupation, he moved from two years of pre-medical studies to work on a tramp steamer and a whaling station, then to Cornell to earn a BA in English with summers spent as a ranger in Yellowstone Park, and finally to employment as a salesman for a rubber company in Peru, Bolivia and Ecuador. By the time he was in his early thirties he and his wife Ruth had fallen in love with South America and with Ecuador in particular, where they started a ranch on the eastern slopes of the Andes. Naming it their "Hacienda Rio Negro", they began to grow coffee, castor beans and other plants.

Gill explored the surrounding jungle and studied the customs of the local Indians, soon becoming fascinated by their use of the jungle pharmacopoeia. After gaining the friendship of local tribal chiefs he was able to witness the preparation of the arrow poison by their witch-doctors. He became firmly convinced that many of the jungle drugs could have a place in modern medicine.

Shortly before a planned holiday to the States in 1932 he had a fall from his horse on one of the jungle trails, a fall which he always insisted was the cause of neurological symptoms which he developed soon afterwards. This eventually led to almost total paralysis and months in a hospital bed in Washington. Although he never accepted the final diagnosis of multiple sclerosis, he was electrified by his neurologist's statement that the muscle spasms common in this disease and in other spastic states might be relieved if only predictable supplies of the arrow poison curare could be made available. No other incentive was needed. 'If only enough curare were available... if only...' he repeated to himself over and over again as he lay in his hospital bed. He had seen curare prepared and had already fully accepted the value of the jungle medicines. If curare might help both himself and others, paralysed or not, he must somehow go back to the jungle and get it. Totally supported by his wife, he undertook months of relentless rehabilitation, re-learning how to regain the use of his fingers and arms and then to walk on crutches. Re-education for his mind followed as he prepared himself technically for his self-imposed task, picking the brains of doctors, pharmacists and botanists and poring over the literature from every related field.

During an almost five year long search for possible financial backing for an expedition both he and his wife turned to writing and publishing. Their efforts included numerous stories about curare, the customs of the Ecuadorian Indian tribes, adventure tales for children set in South America and a long article by Ruth Gill which appeared in the *National Geographic* magazine in 1934.[15]

Their persistence eventually paid off, for a wealthy Massachusetts business-man, Sayre Merrill, read one of the stories about curare and invited Gill for a visit, afterwards agreeing to back an expedition. Further months of preparation followed, until finally in 1938, six years after they had left Ecuador, they returned to their sadly run-down ranch, Gill himself walking with the aid of a cane. After restoring the property as best they could, they set about recruiting personnel for the expedition, which eventually consisted of Gill and his wife, three Ecuadorian assistants, seventy-five porters, thirty-six mules, twelve canoes with their own crews and ten tons of equipment.

The expedition started at the ranch, due east from the twenty-thousand-foot Chimborazo which von Humboldt had attempted to climb, descended the remainder of the Andean wall to the rain forest and river rapids, then travelled along one of the tributaries of the Pastaza River. The hazardous twenty-day journey is described by Gill in his 1940 book *White Water and Black Magic*.[16]

They set up camp, including a basic field laboratory, near an Indian village in the Pastaza valley, their lodgings shared in harmony with tarantulas, suaba ants and scorpions. Once settled in, after much traditional bargaining with colourful trade goods, the place '...became something of a three ring circus for the Indians of the entire region'. No fewer than seven different curare makers arrived at different times:

> *...jungle magic was at its height in making curare, the flying death.*
> *It took time and unending energy to convince the makers that I*
> *already knew something of its magic, and was among them in*
> *friendship and with gifts to learn the rest.... Although I finally was*
> *able to evolve my own technique for producing an adequate curare*

15. Gill, R. "Mrs Robinson Crusoe in Ecuador." *National Geographic* 1934; **65**, 2: 133-172.

16. Gill, R. C. *White Water and Black Magic*. New York, Holt, 1940.

unadulterated by superstition and the extraneous ingredients –
either too toxic or else inert – demanded by that same superstition,
I could not do it without the witchmen.[17]

The expedition spent nearly five months at camp. Each small botanical detail was observed, simple field experiments carried out, dried specimens of every ingredient obtained – not only the arrow poisons but also many other of the remedies of the witch doctors. Ruth Gill cooked for them all in an oven put together from two empty gasoline cans, keeping full records in her field notebooks.

At the end of 1938 they returned to the United States with dozens of crated specimens and twenty-five pounds of different kinds of crude curare – all accurately documented for the first time at the point of collection – by far the largest amount brought out of the jungle to that point. Even then it was still not plain sailing, for Gill continues:

...our trials were not at an end even after the expedition succeeded
in bringing back the curare material. For some time it was discour-
agingly difficult to find a reputable manufacturer who was willing
to accept the new field evidence, and to pioneer the refining and
biological standardisation of the curare on anything approaching
an adequate and ethically sound basis.[18]

Through the auspices of Dr A. E. Bennett at the University of Nebraska, however, biological standardisation of Gill's raw product was finally undertaken there by A. R. McIntyre and after further work by the Squibb Company the preparation "Intocostrin", Squibb's extract of crude curare, became available. After preliminary disappointing work in cases of spastic paralysis, in which only temporary improvement occurred, Dr Bennett excitedly reported: 'I think we have made a ten strike in the use of curare.'[19]

This referred to its use in modifying the seizures of convulsive shock therapy, first induced by intravenous injections of the drug metrazol and then later by electro-shock. Bennett's paper detailing the use of Intocostrin in over a hundred cases was published in 1940 and a dramatic film comparing shock therapy in anaesthetised and unanaesthetised patients shown that June at the meeting of the American Medical Association. A physician working for Squibb, Lewis Wright, began to promote the

---

17. Gill, R. C. *ibid.*, p. 320.

18. Gill, R. C. *ibid.*, p. 355.

19. Smith, P. *Arrows of Mercy*, New York, Doubleday, 1969, p. 138.

idea that the drug might have a place in anaesthesia.[20] Several laughed outright at this suggestion, but two – both of whom later became major figures in American anaesthesia – agreed to try it out. Although he was later to become one of the early workers with curare, Stuart Cullen was dismayed by his initial experiments with dogs and after nearly killing most of his animals he dismissed the drug as still unsafe for use in humans. The first attempts by Emanuel Papper to use it in two patients were equally alarming, resulting, as he put it, 'in my being up half the night giving artificial respiration'. As a result Papper also deemed it far too dangerous. It was left to a then little-known Canadian anaesthetist, Harold Griffith, to show that it could be safely given. After dismissing the idea as "fantastic" when it was first broached, Griffith got the chance to talk with Bennett about his success with psychiatric patients and decided to give the Intocostrin a trial. He did not tell the patient on January 23rd 1942, a young man with acute appendicitis, nor the surgeon. He certainly never considered informing the hospital authorities in Montreal that he planned to use an untried and potentially very dangerous drug. There was no such thing as informed consent in those days, or hospital ethics committees. Either it would work or it wouldn't.

I have a copy of that first anaesthetic record. There is no mention of the respiration being assisted in any way, though the surgeon commented after the fact on how easy the operation had seemed. Griffith and his young resident Enid Johnson went on to use curare in twenty-six patients, before publishing their results with this modest claim:

> *...We have been so impressed by the dramatic effect produced in every one of our patients, that we believe the investigation should be continued... It seems to us that curare may prove to be a drug which will occasionally be of great value, and will give us the means of providing the surgeon with excellent muscular relaxation at critical times.*[21]

Others began to use the curare extract as a supplement to light general anaesthesia, and two years later Ralph Waters reported further on its use in abdominal surgery. Although the world was still at war the Atlantic could now be crossed by air and some limited supplies of the Squibb product made a much speedier journey in the

20. Wright's promotion of Intocostrin was an integral part of the final phase of the curare story, his influence extending even into the southern hemisphere. While on service with the US Navy he gave a sample of the drug to Harry Daly in Australia which led to Daly being the first to use curare in anaesthesia in that country in 1945.

21. Griffith, H. R. and Johnson, E. "The use of curare in general anesthesia." *Anesthesiology* 1942; **3**: 418-420.

hands of physicians in the American air force than the news of ether had done close to a century before. Cecil Gray, whom I first encountered in the 1960s as both an examiner and a lecturer, very kindly recorded his memories of those days for me on cassette.[22]

John Halton was serving as medical officer to a barrage balloon unit in the northwest of England and heard about the use of Intocostrin during off-duty contacts with American officers based at Warrington. They promised him a small amount for his own use, which he later shared with Gray. They used the drug quite independently, concluding by the time their supplies ran out that its action appeared to be somewhat unpredictable. Getting together later over a glass of beer they remembered and talked about the curare which they had used during practical physiology experiments as undergraduates and decided to see if some of it might still be available:

> We went down to see Rod Gregory, then the senior lecturer in Physiology at Liverpool and later as Professor to become world famous as the person who first isolated the hormone "gastrin". He was always a man to encourage clinicians and he became very excited. Through his auspices Burroughs Welcome gave us a white powder labelled "curarine", which they informed us was pure. We autoclaved the powder, shook it up till it dissolved in bottles of saline and dripped it into patients. The results were dramatic, of course, and we soon found an optimum dose, in my own investigations with abdominal cases and John with his thoracic patients. We compared notes frequently and then joined forces to present our results.[23]

Their landmark paper[24] introduced a completely new technique, one that helped transform anaesthesia from the old art into the science it is today. They used a combination of drugs, each with a specific purpose, to produce what they termed "balanced anaesthesia". D-tubocurarine, the active ingredient of the liana *Chondodendron tomentosum*, was employed not simply as an aid to anaesthesia as had been done earlier with the crude extract, but in larger doses as an essential part of the technique to produce total paralysis and allow complete control of ventilation. Although differ-

---

22. T. C. Gray, personal communication 1982.

23. T. C. Gray, *ibid*.

24. Gray, T. C. and Halton, J. "A milestone in anaesthesia? (D-tubocurarine chloride)." *Proc R Soc Med* 1946; **39**: 400-408.

ent agents have come and gone, the fundamentals of balanced anaesthesia remain the same today.[25]

Yet what might have happened had the supplies of crude curare not been made available late in 1938? I asked that question of Cecil Gray. He felt that the whole timetable of medicine would have been quite seriously affected. With little progress possible during the war and the increasing concern of the new regulatory bodies on both sides of the Atlantic in post-war years over the uncontrolled use of new drugs, the "give it and see" type of groundbreaking work done by Griffith would not have been allowed, and without this stimulus their own work and that of others in the United States would simply not have been undertaken. Although the technique of controlled manual ventilation under deep cyclopropane anaesthesia was already in use,[26] the very significant advances in thoracic and cardiac surgery which became feasible only after the introduction of the muscle relaxants might have been delayed for one or even two decades. Many developments in the early days of intensive care, in which the relaxants came to play an increasing role, major organ transplantation and who knows what else would have been included in such delay. We can only speculate on a totally different course of events.

The pioneers in this fascinating story have been rewarded in the fickle manner typical of history. Alexander von Humboldt had the vision in the early 1800s to realise that curare would be tamed, "if the constituents could be obtained without being confounded together from the places where they are prepared". The Gill-Merrill expedition did exactly that, allowing the completion of the investigation von Humboldt had forecast over a century previously. He lived into his eighties, honoured during his own lifetime for his scientific achievements, particularly in geography and geology, and accorded a state funeral in Berlin, his name kept alive today through the Humboldt Current which flows along the west coast of South America. Charles Waterton dreamt of controlling what he termed the 'frightful spasms' of rabies. He had much of the reasoning right including the need to prevent the asphyxia which resulted from these spasms. In time the muscle relaxants came to play a major role in the treatment of different seizure states and in a host of other conditions and situations where the airway is compromised.

Wouralia the donkey received the best reward of all, perhaps, a long and contented twenty-five-year retirement on the pastures of Walton Hall. Looking out over the lake on the day of my visit I wondered where she was buried, for she had

---

25. Although Gray and Halton's paper came to be a landmark study, equally important work was undertaken by others on both sides of the Atlantic. A fine summary of these contributions can be found in an editorial by John Utting entitled "The era of relaxant anaesthesia" in the *British Journal of Anaesthesia* 1992; **69**, 6: 551-553.

26. Cecil Gray commented on the profound depression of respiration produced by such a technique.

unwittingly set the stage for the future. She was given a large dose of the poison. So were Gray and Halton's patients, the only difference being that they had first received a hypnotic drug to render them unconscious. Wouralia underwent a tracheotomy, her breathing supported with air through the nozzle of an ancient bellows. Each of Gray and Halton's patients had an endotracheal tube placed in their windpipes for exactly the same purpose, with a rubber bag controlling their ventilation and maintaining unconsciousness with a mixture of nitrous oxide and oxygen. Wouralia's lungs were inflated by the bellows until she could hold her head up and look around. The patients in the "milestone in anaesthesia" study were similarly ventilated until their curare had begun to wear off, at which point the recovery to full muscle function was hastened by the use of an antagonistic drug. Not all that much of a difference!

And the early explorers – von Humboldt, Waterton, Brodie, Sewell, Bernard, King, Gill, Bennett, Griffith and all the rest – they were simply forward thinkers along the way to balanced anaesthesia, with Gray and Halton helping to find the right place for one of the last pieces of the puzzle, at which point the harnessing of curare did become a milestone – not just in anaesthesia, but also in medicine, a milestone to rank alongside the coming of anaesthesia and antisepsis in the nineteenth century and the discoveries of penicillin and the antibiotics in the twentieth.

Harold Griffith went on to make an enormous contribution in research and training in anaesthesia, and was widely honoured internationally, while Arthur Läwen, who thirty and more years before had understood much more than Griffith about the combination of curare and anaesthesia – his work came at the wrong time and is largely forgotten. And what of Gill, how has history treated him? His story gives confirmation of the role that serendipity can play. Starting from a seemingly hopeless position, flat on his back and paralysed in a hospital bed, with no money and only a rudimentary practical knowledge of the arrow poison, he pondered on the words 'if only there were enough curare in the civilised world to enable it to be standardised biologically, so that safe doses could be gauged'. Chance had taken him into the world of the witch doctor, chance then to a hospital bed, and it was a chance remark from his doctor that led him to the Pastaza valley.

Hans Selye, who pioneered much of our understanding of stress, wrote that two things were necessary to make a great dream come true, the first a capacity to dream, the second persistence – a faith in that dream. Gill had both these qualities in full measure, systematically planning and carrying through a very personal and unique contribution. And if you consider the sequence over several centuries, the initial horror, amazement and even bewilderment of the voyageurs, the thought and experimentation of the explorers, the scientific investigation which eventually followed, the years then of frustration and the final introduction into medicine, it seems to me that the whole story of the flying death is worthy of remembrance as a great dream which finally did come true.

The story of Richard Gill did not have a happy ending. Although the value of his work was readily acknowledged by Bennett and Griffith, he felt that his claim to have been responsible for the first clinically adequate curare was never publicly recognised. Envisioning himself at the centre of a multi-million dollar industry, he became very frustrated and bitter when he was shut out of the major commercial development of the drug. When his expansive plans for a flourishing business in Ecuador collapsed he managed to maintain an agent there, and then despite a worsening spastic paralysis of his lower limbs he engaged a full-time chemist, setting up in the garage of his home in Palo Alto what he called 'the only arrow poison factory in the world'. Within a year they had developed their own process for extracting the pure alkaloid and were able to export a limited supply to a number of countries, particularly to Germany. His final goal was to find a slow-acting form of the drug for use in spastic paralysis and in 1953 he produced a tablet for sub-lingual use[27] which he claimed would complete the final taming of curare – and make his fortune into the bargain. Unfortunately he failed to secure any commercial interest in this product, and when he died at the comparatively early age of fifty-seven Richard Cochran Gill was a disappointed man, even paranoid about those who surrounded him.

I have been fortunate to view copies of his original 16mm films and to listen to his persuasive and somewhat flowery style of speech on a recording of a radio interview in Palo Alto. It was a privilege, too, to talk at length about him with Bill Neff and Violet Ohlsen. Their combined memories almost made me feel as though I had known him, an illusion cemented by the picture on my study wall. Just as they had done in 1938, his compelling eyes look out across a steaming batch of poison, a jungle helmet nonchalantly posed in the background on the top of a cane.

Time has not yet balanced the scales. Only one author[28] devotes anything more than just a few lines to his work, while a botanical review even claimed that his book was largely a figment of his imagination. The pages of *White Water and Black Magic* and the 16mm films of the expedition combine to totally refute such nonsense.[29] Perhaps history will one day agree unreservedly with Griffith's verdict:

---

27. I still have a small quantity of those 3 mgm tablets, given to me by Bill Neff.

28. Smith, P. *Arrows of Mercy*, New York, Doubleday, 1969.

29. See also Humble, R. M. "The Gill-Merrill Expedition – Penultimate Chapter in the Curare story." *Anesthesiology* 1982; **57**, 6: 519-526.

*I believe that your work with curare has been a great contribution
to modern medicine.*[30]

One postscript needs to be added to this story, for it is all too easy to become purblind, extolling only the merits of workers from one's own cultural background. The use of muscle relaxants in modern medicine could never have happened without the earliest work of all. The concoctions of the South American Indians were made and modified by trial and error. They tested their products on live animals in the field. Guesswork you may say – or tradition handed down through many generations. But trial and error and work with animals are part and parcel of research in pharmacology. Although many inactive and unnecessary ingredients found their way into the "black pitche" of the different tribes and regions, the witch doctors were no less important as pioneering field scientists than those who were to follow. Without their very early experiments curare could still be unknown today; without them anaesthesia and surgery might well have developed in very different ways.

---

30. Letter from Harold R. Griffith to Richard C. Gill dated June 30th 1943, from correspondence kindly made available to the author by the Arthur E. Guedel Memorial Anesthesia Center, San Francisco.

HARVEST DELAYED

Like one who has scattered abroad the Avena[31] fatua of
knowledge, from which neither branch nor blossom nor
fruit has resulted,
I am in need of the consolation of a friend.
Thomas Beddoes to Humphrey Davy, December 1808

I f the story of curare spans more than four centuries, the evolution of modern anaesthesia must be measured in terms of millennia. Evidence of attempts to relieve the pain of surgical procedures can be found in the artefacts of most primitive societies and also in those of the early civilisations of the Middle East, Greece, Rome and the Orient. A variety of curious physical methods, the power of mind over matter, time honoured anodynes – all were explored, with some occasional limited success. Details of these early efforts can be found in many sources, notably in *Ancient Anodynes*.[32] Although further discussion remains outside the scope of this small volume, continued emphasis on the relevance of history does not.

The noted medical historian Henry Sigerist has written that "medical history teaches us where we come from, where we stand at the present time, and in what direction we are marching; it is the compass that guides us into the future". A review of a few highlights from the emerging speciality of anaesthesia will help to demonstrate how such a compass may work; it will also provide a base from the past to bring out the remarkable repetitive patterns which are typical of every branch of history.

Whilst the early explorers and investigators continued their attempts to unravel the mysteries of the South American rain forest during the seventeenth and eighteenth centuries, there was much discussion on the other side of the Atlantic about the composition of atmospheric air and the nature of respiration. This led to the discovery of carbon dioxide, nitrous oxide and eventually oxygen, with Lavoisier in Paris soon propounding correct theories of respiration and combustion. He was too

---

31. *Avena* (Latin) – oats or wild oats.

32. Ellis, E. S. *Ancient Anodynes*. London, Heinemann, 1946.

successful for his own good. The revolutionaries cut his head off. 'The Republic has no need of chemists,' said Robespierre.

The identification of the various gases led to the introduction of "pneumatic" medicine, and not long before Alexander von Humboldt viewed the preparation of curare in Venezuela patients started to flock to the Pneumatic Institution in the west of England to be treated for a wide variety of conditions by the so called "factitious airs". Oxygen became known as "vital air", carbon dioxide as "fixed air", hydrogen as "inflammable air", nitrogen as "azotic air" and carbon monoxide as "hydrocarbonate". All were diluted to a greater or lesser extent with atmospheric air, with the usual remedies of the time occasionally being added, including ether.

The driving force behind the Bristol Institution[33] was Thomas Beddoes. I cannot think of this fascinating individual – classical scholar, chemist and physician rolled into one – without wanting to place him alongside the great characters created by Dickens. Beddoes would fit well into the pages of *The Pickwick Papers* or *Great Expectations* – very short, extremely fat, red-faced and prone to apoplexy. Consumed by enthusiasm, he was an eternal optimist who passionately believed that these new airs would be the answer to all the ills of mankind. While looking for staff to aid him in the work of the Institution, the name of Humphrey Davy was brought to his attention. Although only twenty, Davy had already been studying nitrous oxide and despite his youth had also had the temerity to produce a textbook on chemistry. When the Institution opened in 1799 he experimented on himself with all the known gases, nearly killing himself on one occasion with carbon monoxide. He worked particularly with nitrous oxide, inhaling it frequently to experience all of its effects. In a small volume describing his researches[34] he later made the famous observation that since nitrous oxide 'appears capable of destroying physical pain, it may probably be used with advantage during surgical operations...' No one followed up directly on this suggestion, however, and Davy moved on to greater fame in the world of chemistry.

When enthusiasm at his Institution began to flag, Beddoes transferred his energy into the area of preventive medicine, but once again his ideas failed to catch on. Like many who were to follow him he died a disappointed man, frustrated that his great ideas had led to nothing, and just a day before his death on Christmas Eve, 1808, he opened his soul to his protégé in disconsolate words. It seemed that no great advances would come through the medium of these factitious airs. Yet looking at their subsequent history, the seeds had already been planted towards a harvest beyond Beddoes' wildest dreams.

---

33. See Cartwright, F. F. *The English Pioneers of Anaesthesia*. Bristol, Wright, 1952.

34. Davy, H. *Researches Chemical and Physiological*. Bristol, Biggs and Cottle, 1800.

Reading the bare facts of the story now it is hard to imagine how the discovery of anaesthesia was still several decades away. The loss of the sensation of pain from nitrous oxide was demonstrated before one of the most prominent London surgeons of the early nineteenth century, and by this time also there was recognition of the profound state of lethargy that could be produced by ether when inhaled as a treatment for asthma. Yet the delay is not really surprising given the social climate of the times. Life in Britain was cheap. Children worked for a pittance in mines and textile mills, stealing a rabbit remained a capital offence and pain itself had a strong association with divine retribution for sin. Little wonder then that amputations were performed with a premium on speed, with fortitude the main solace for patients. Progress varied widely in different cultures. Whilst Seisha Hanaoka performed radical breast surgery in Japan in the early 1800s, achieving remarkable results in patients sedated by a mixture of his own devising containing hyoscine, hyoscyamine, atropine and anconite, in Europe the female novelist Fanny Burney left an extraordinary account of her complete consciousness during a mastectomy. Her detailed description of the procedure makes for particularly chilling reading as she tells how the knife of the famous army surgeon Baron Larrey scraped against her breast bone. The anguish of all such patients is also reflected by the fact that around the same period an operation bell continued to ring out along the corridors of London's University College Hospital, its purpose to summon attendants to forcibly restrain patients during surgery. Western society was still not quite ready to move forward.

A MAN FROM THE EAST

Gentlemen, this Yankee dodge beats Mesmerism hollow.
Robert Liston, December 21st 1846

The doctrine of "vitalism", or "animal magnetism" as it was later known, swept through the upper echelons of Parisian society towards the turn of the nineteenth century. Franz Anton Mesmer came to believe that the healing force emanated from within himself and though his theories were denounced by colleagues as having no medical basis, his early work was further developed by others under the eponymous term of "mesmerism". By 1829 the technique had been successfully employed by Cloquet for a mastectomy, but an uproar followed a decade later when a similar method was used for an amputation. The patient had been trained to resist pain, the establishment claimed, with the prominent London surgeon, Robert Liston, leading the opposition to this "quackery". Believers in the new approach later contended that their idea of procuring insensibility for surgical operations had forced society to look for other means to the same end.

When he confirmed the efficacy of ether anaesthesia in London in December 1846, following the first successful public demonstration two months earlier in Boston, Massachusetts, Robert Liston afforded the word "mesmerism" a mocking accolade, little realising the place it would eventually find in the realm of psycho-somatic medicine. We do not hear much of surgery under mesmerism or hypnotism nowadays, but I have known more than one anaesthetist who has used hypnosis successfully, certainly for minor surgery, and almost unknowingly many of us learned to harness some of its principles in our practice whilst inducing anaesthesia in young children by purely inhalational means. That it remains a powerful tool in our modern world is illustrated by a story of an incident which took place a few years after my second Irish sojourn. It is wonderfully told by the Malaysian physician concerned:[35]

> *I was working as a consultant psychiatrist at St Brigid's Hospital,*
> *Ardee, near Dublin. I loved to ride during my off duty time and*

---

35.   Dr M. Mahadevan, personal communication 1996.

boarded horses in County Meath, next to Tom Dreaper's famous Greenogue stables where he trained the legendary steeplechaser Arkle. Not many people in the area knew that I was a doctor. Seeing me only on horseback on the weekends, I suspect that some of the locals considered me a bit mysterious, perhaps a Maharajah or the younger son of a decadent eastern potentate!

After riding my friends and I used to gather for a drink at the Hunter's Moon in Ashbourne. We were there one Saturday night in June 1965. Being close to the summer solstice the sun did not set until very late, almost till midnight, and in the fast-fading twilight the manager of a local branch of the Bank of Ireland failed to spot a cattle truck parked at the top of a hill a short distance from the pub, crashing his car into the other vehicle whilst driving home to Dublin with his family. Bystanders rushed to the Hunter's Moon on the chance of finding a doctor, and naturally I responded.

It was not a pretty scene. The banker was bleeding profusely from multiple lacerations to the face and head. His wife, in her mid-fifties, had died instantly, her brain shattered, while one daughter in the late stages of her first pregnancy appeared to be breathing her last. They were talking about doing a Caesarean section on the spot in an effort to save the child. Under the circumstances this simply wasn't possible, however, and the young mother died along with her unborn infant. Another daughter in the car had been less seriously injured.

I attended to their father in the very poor light. He was in great pain, and very agitated, almost hysterical, groaning and talking about the accident, guilty that he had caused the crash and very worried about his wife, his daughter and the fate of their first grandchild. With all these things running through his mind he became extremely restless, and as the heavy bleeding continued I tried to help him in the only way I could. I told him I was a doctor, a psychiatrist, but though I didn't have a pin or a pill with me, if he could manage to co-operate I would try to relax him.

'Oh,' he was able to respond, 'you're a man from the East!' His ready acceptance of my background, even while critically injured, may have given an extra dimension to my subsequent efforts.

'Hold on to my hand, I'll try and relax you,' I told him. 'Just take normal deep breaths, and as I count slowly from one to ten you'll start to go into a deep, relaxed and comfortable sleep. All

your pain, all your anxiety, all your uneasy feelings, everything will go, and you will begin to feel very comfortable and go into a deep sleep.'

I began to count, he began to cooperate, and within a few short minutes he was able to drift into a deep sleep. By clicking my fingers I kept calling him out of his sleep, making sure he was still conscious and aware, checking his pulse and then sending him back once again.

'Every time I click my fingers you will experience a deeper and deeper relaxed state,' I said, being forced at the same time to tell him that his wife and daughter had survived the accident, that everything was fine and that he would wake up with no pain or discomfort. As I continued to talk to him he became less agitated, more calm, his breathing slowed down and he was able to gain relief from all those things and thoughts which were pressing upon him. At the same time his pulse also slowed and strengthened and the bleeding lessened very significantly. When the ambulance eventually arrived the attendants were able to extract him carefully from the wreckage, taking him off then with the other daughter to Dublin.

I drove back to my own hospital, where I was in residence, and was fast asleep in the early hours of the morning when the telephone rang. It was from the Gardai, asking if I was the doctor with a car with the number ...99 who had attended to a crashed and injured victim outside the Hunter's Moon at Ashbourne the previous night.

I said 'Yes, of course,' and the caller asked me to phone the surgeon or anaesthetist at the Mater Hospital in Dublin as soon as possible, which I did. The surgeon sounded greatly annoyed.

'How could you sedate a man with a head injury?' he began. I replied to the effect that I had not sedated him.

'But he complains of no pain whatsoever, despite the obvious head injuries he sustained a couple of hours ago and is sleepy and sedated. We must assess his neurological state properly before taking him to the operating theatre to see what has happened, check where he is bleeding from and so on. We cannot do this properly after the use of sedative drugs. I would like to know your name and all your particulars. If anything should happen to this man I shall certainly report you. You should not have sedated him.' I was quite

unable to convince him that I had used no drugs of any kind, so I simply gave him my details and went back to sleep.

In the morning I was woken by a loud banging on my door. It was my boss, the Superintendent of the hospital, a first class psychiatrist and wonderful teacher who taught me a lot.

'Wake up, Devan, wake up,' he shouted, 'you are in the papers. Malaysian psychiatrist hypnotises crash victim. Get up quickly, and read it for yourself!'

He was so delighted that his hospital had been put on the map and all the other Ardee people were very enthusiastic and supportive. Much publicity followed and I even got a call from the Malaysian Government. They told me the Prime Minister was very happy. 'Please come back home... we need you here,' they said.

By the Monday morning it seemed that everyone was happy. Everyone but me, that is, because I realised that my patient's wife and daughter had been killed, contrary to what I had told him. So the next day I went to see him at the Mater Hospital. As there had been no underlying cerebral injury and he was fully alert, I was able to discuss the fact that I had given him false information by post-hypnotic suggestion.

'I told you under the hypnosis that your wife was well and your daughter all right, just to calm you. Otherwise you were so agitated and restless, that you might even have bled to death. I had simply no other way to settle you down.'

He thanked me profusely and agreed with my proposal to re-hypnotise him to reinforce the reality of the accident by further post hypnotic suggestion. Being a very willing subject I again put him easily into a hypnotic state, telling him then that his wife had passed away, his daughter too had passed away, but that he had survived the crash along with his other daughter and had much to look forward to. After all this was finished we chatted for a while, and before I left the hospital we went on to talk a bit about my plans, what I was going to do with my career.

The story did not end there. First I got a call from the British Medical and Dental Hypnosis Society, asking me to go to England to present a paper on hypnosis in relation to haemorrhage. Next, since I had taken some of my training in India, the Indian Government tried to claim part of the credit for my success. More calls from Malaysia followed and the story eventually appeared in articles in several magazine.

The biggest surprise came a few weeks later. I received a call from a bank to inform me that a significant sum of money would be deposited monthly in an account in my name, for the next two years, with the intention of allowing me to undertake further post-graduate study in the United States. The donor wished to remain anonymous and the bank remained very tight-lipped about the whole affair. Although I was able to use some of the funds to travel to the States, to Harvard first and later to California to visit a successful alcohol and drug addiction programme, a family tragedy soon necessitated my permanent return to Malaysia.

I had the privilege of meeting the narrator of this story at the wedding of his niece in Canmore, Alberta in 1996. My wife and I and another Irish friend subsequently spent a great day with him at the du Maurier International at Spruce Meadows, just outside Calgary, the richest event in the world of professional show-jumping. Many things were evident that day: Devan was a wonderful raconteur; he had never lost his love of horses, for we discussed his keen interest in breeding and lifelong involvement with the Perak Turf Club and the Malaysian Polo Association; he had never forgotten the friends and memories of his time in Ireland; and the early professional promise had only been the prelude to a very distinguished career.

THE FINAL PIECES

And that farthest bottle labelled 'Ether'
Is the house o'ertopping all.
from *Confessions* by Robert Browning

However loud the protests of the establishment of the day in regard to mesmerism, surgery without pain had been shown to be possible. Then around the time of the publication of Waterton's book on his wanderings came the unfulfilled work of Henry Hickman. Using guinea pigs for his experiments, this young English physician set out to relieve the pain of surgery by inhalational means. Although he gained the support of Baron Larrey in France, few others were prepared to listen to his theories on "suspended animation" or to give much credit to his work with carbon dioxide and possibly also with nitrous oxide.

As Claude Bernard in Paris took the curare story one step further through his remarkable experiments with the frog, the arena moved from the realms of science and experimentation into the worlds of public and private entertainment. By the 1840s it cost the public only a few pennies or cents to watch male volunteers staggering around a stage under the influence of nitrous oxide, "laughing gas" as it became known, and the habit of ether-sniffing spread into polite social gatherings on both sides of the Atlantic. Witnessing the "frolics" which could follow the inhalation of ether vapour led the Atlanta physician Crawford Long to undertake minor surgery in 1842 after rendering patients unconscious with the aid of ether dropped on a handkerchief. Although failing to publicise his intermittent successes with this practice, Long is fully deserving of an honoured place in the annals of surgery and anaesthesia.

The public stage was now almost set and progress became inevitable when dentists began to look for ways to relieve the pain of their advancing art. The story of the travelling showman, Gardner Quincey Colton, and the very perceptive dentist in his Hartford, Connecticut audience is well known. If a man could crack his shin and make it bleed while under the influence of this laughing gas and give no apparent sign of having felt the injury, Horace Wells surmised that its inhalation should relieve the pain of extraction of a tooth. Just one day later he became the subject in a successful demonstration of that very fact. He rushed to promote the method following a number of further private experiments, but withdrew the gas too quickly during an arranged public demonstration in Boston in January 1845, his pioneering efforts rewarded by his being hissed and booed out of the operating room to cries of 'humbug'. Although continuing to use the gas, Wells' career and life descended into tragedy and eventual suicide at the age of thirty-three, a much worse fate than had befallen Courvoisier, and it was left to his erstwhile partner, William Thomas Green Morton, to bring these pioneering efforts to a successful conclusion. In what is now known as the Ether Dome of the old Massachusetts General Hospital, on October 16th 1846, he induced a sufficient level of surgical anaesthesia with the vapour of ether to allow surgeon John Warren to remove a tumour from the neck of patient Gilbert Abbott. History and politics are replete with memorable utterances. Medicine has only a few, two relating to anaesthesia standing out particularly. One was spoken on this day, Ether Day as it is still celebrated in Boston, when after inserting the last stitch Warren favoured his audience with these five words: 'Gentlemen, this is no humbug!'

That scene has been wonderfully captured by Hinckley in his oil on canvas painting, *First Operation Under Ether*, which hangs in the Countway Library in Boston, and Morton's epitaph can still be read on a visit to Mount Auburn Cemetery in the same city. It describes him as the "inventor and revealer of anaesthetic inhalation, by whom pain in surgery was averted and annulled, before whom in all time surgery was agony, since whom science has control of pain". Some have questioned Morton's legacy because he initially tried to keep the nature of his agent secret and later attempted to procure a patent for it. In the larger picture of things he was simply another connection along the way, his efforts just another piece of the giant puzzle which we are still working on today.

Events then moved rapidly. By the following month major surgery had been successfully performed under ether anaesthesia and it did not take long for such news to spread to the Old World. James Y. Simpson heard of Liston's successful amputation in London and within a month he had administered ether to a patient in labour in Edinburgh, further cases precipitating a debate about the nature and purpose of the pain of childbirth. Then after personal experimentation towards the end of 1847 with the recently discovered chloroform, Simpson moved on to the use of this new agent in obstetrics, his grandiose purpose "to banish pain from the lying-in centres of the world". And so although the true rise of surgery had to wait a few more decades until the principles of antisepsis were understood, the three forerunners of our modern practice had now made their appearance.

While the response to the unsuccessful public demonstration caused the first of these – nitrous oxide – to leave the stage for a while, within two decades it had made a resounding comeback, not least through the work of the itinerant showman and lecturer who turned himself into an itinerant anaesthetist. Gardner Quincey Colton, whose exhibition in Hartford had so triggered the imagination of Horace Wells, went on to give thousands relief from the pain of dental extractions, even founding his own Colton Dental Association and never failing to give full credit to Wells. The remarkable history of nitrous oxide has been splendidly told by W. D. A. Smith.[36] With its use now steadily decreasing in our own times, if Davy, Wells and Colton were flies on the wall today they might be astonished to hear of its transformation from anaesthetic gas to greenhouse gas![37]

Chloroform, third in the early chronology, brought both success and controversy, a quicker and smoother induction of anaesthesia compared to ether being offset by occasional sudden deaths and by the later recognition of liver toxicity. Countless numbers benefited greatly, however, and it remained in regular use for more than a hundred years.

And what of di-ethyl ether, second in line but first in terms of the real break-through? Although patients liked neither the smell nor the irritant nature of its vapour, it possessed one important advantage, a high margin of safety even in inexpert hands. As we look back now all the way to 1846 it might be true to say that ether deserves an individual accolade as "the house o'ertopping all".[38]

36. Smith, W. D. A. *Under the Influence – A History of Nitrous Oxide and Oxygen Anesthesia.* London, Macmillan, 1982.

37. In part due to its production in the use of fertilisers in agriculture, nitrous oxide is now recognised as a significant contributor to the greenhouse gas effect.

38. Different interpretations of Browning's poem "Confessions" have been suggested. I am using his words here purely in the context of my story.

LESSONS
ANCIENT AND MODERN

That which is new at this time will one day be ancient,
as what is ancient was once new.
Augustin Belloste (1654-1730)

When I came back from Africa in the early 1960s to learn more about anaesthesia I walked in on a heated debate. It concerned what was referred to as "the educated hand" of the anaesthetist. Intermittent positive pressure ventilators, the successors to the older cuirass and tank ventilators[39] which had saved many patients during the polio epidemics of the fifties, were now becoming widely used in operating rooms. The pride and joy of Norman Eve at Whipps Cross was an old and very large Engström machine which he had managed to acquire through Swedish contacts.

'Disastrous,' said the traditionalists; 'we must not lose the feel of the educated hand on the reservoir bag, the direct link between the anaesthetist and the minute-to-minute changes in the compliance of the patient's lungs. A machine can never replace such a personal touch.'

'Nonsense,' replied the modernists; 'the anaesthetist's hands are now freed for the many other tasks necessary for control of all aspects of the ongoing anaesthesia.'

The debate went on in such a vein for many months, strange to look back on today when a young trainee might find it hard to imagine a routine practice during major surgery that relied solely on manual control of respiration. My registrar colleague, Bill Chew, had remarkable dexterity. Whilst involved in a variety of activities which required the use of both hands, such as the changing of intravenous bottles or drawing up drugs into syringes, he found little difficulty in using his foot to continue the intermittent squeezing of the reservoir bag – after first dropping it to the floor. (For the benefit of lay readers I should explain that this bag stayed attached to the anaesthetic machine through a long rubber extension hose.) My brain never permitted such separation of purpose between hand and foot, so with often no access to a ventilator the artificial respiration had to be temporarily suspended, anathema to

---

39. Commonly known as "iron lungs".

both teacher and trainee today. One learned to do things quickly, and as "simultane-ously" as possible.

In the light of the advances of the past four decades and with ventilators now available for use in every sector of society the educated hand controversy seems absurd. Yet the tenor of the debate was nothing new. Go back to the turn of the century and the development of the early anaesthetic record charts.[40] When the regular measurement of the blood pressures of anaesthetised patients came to be advocated precisely the same arguments were made, the traditionalists even using the very same expression: 'The time required to take blood pressure readings with these newfangled instruments will lead to the loss of the educated finger on the pulse.'

Now go back another four decades. One aspect then of the debate over the safe administration of chloroform was whether or not to feel the pulse! John Snow in London, who understood the science of anaesthesia many generations before that phrase was ever thought of, combined the meticulous administration of regulated amounts of chloroform with careful monitoring of both pulse and respiration. Further to the north the Edinburgh school under Simpson and Syme took the completely opposite view. Although espousing the sound principles of free admixture with air and the avoidance of respiratory obstruction, they paid little heed to the amount of chloroform used and totally ignored the pulse. Syme described the practice quite succinctly:

> *We are guided as to the effect, not by the circulation, but entirely by the respiration; you never see anybody here with his finger on the pulse while chloroform is given.*[41]

Whatever the subject – to monitor the pulse or not, to lose the educated finger, to lose the educated hand – the same old arguments resurface from time to time. They did so in my own career during a lively debate about the routine use of cardiac and other types of monitoring and in one way or another they will show up again in the future. As computers and operating robots gradually take over perhaps someone will one day bemoan the loss of the educated mind! Nothing very earth shattering in all this, you may think. Simply progress, the natural response to new technologies as the boundaries of our knowledge move forward. But look back again and you will find other recurring patterns.

In the past one hundred and fifty years anaesthesia has been induced and main-tained in a truly astonishing variety of ways: with the use of rubber bags, glass bulbs,

---

40. Initially known as "ether charts".

41. Syme, J. "Remarks on the exhibition of chloroform." *Lancet* Jan 20, 1855, p. 55.

handkerchiefs, sponges, cones and open wire-frame face masks; by means of a large pre-filled cloth bag slung over the anaesthetist's shoulder and later by tubing, even glass inhalers, hung round the anaesthetist's neck; by hand pump and foot pump; by a complicated "anaesthesimeter" and by an elaborate "anaesthetising machine" which employed a wheel, ratchet and handle; and by anything from a delicate weight-balancing mechanism to a steel container which had to be plunged into hot water before use. Surgical procedures were even carried out within the confines of an "anaesthetic car". Allowing the administration of nitrous oxide and oxygen under pressure, as suggested by Paul Bert, this cumbersome looking operating chamber on wheels was used at more than one Paris hospital in 1880.[42]

Following on from an early experiment by John Snow, who administered chloroform to a rabbit via a tracheotomy tube, Trendelenburg, MacEwen, Maydl, O'Dwyer, Kuhn and other innovators introduced and improved the technique of endotracheal anaesthesia. Insufflation and inhalation were advocated, via both pharynx and larynx, using many different catheters and tubes, whilst an array of ingenious valves, vaporisers, circuits and other assorted pieces of equipment came and went, evolving slowly towards the anaesthetic machines and early ventilators of the modern era. Local anaesthesia and local anaesthetic drugs appeared on the scene towards the end of the nineteenth century, then spinal and epidural anaesthesia and still later the intravenous induction agents. The international nature of the roll call of honour from those days is illustrated by a selection of just a few of the names of the individuals involved.[43] Others moved things forward through dangerous self-experimentation, notable among them Stanley Wilson, William Halsted and Edgar "Gar" Pask. Wilson lost his life experimenting with nitrous oxide, Halsted became addicted to cocaine and Pask's extraordinary wartime exploits[44] most certainly affected his subsequent health. Whether contributing through isolated discoveries or innovations, or through the efforts of entire careers, pioneers are usually defined as "the originators of a

---

42. Full information on all the old equipment can be found in Duncum, B. M. *The Development of Inhalation Anaesthesia*. London, Oxford University Press, 1947 and Thomas, K. B. *The Development of Anaesthetic Apparatus*. Oxford, Blackwell, 1975.

43. Clover, Koller, Halsted, Corning, Hewitt, Schleich, Matas, Cathelin, Sicard, Bier, Tuffier, Guedel, McKesson, Magill, Macintosh, Labat, Boyle, Waters, Heidbrink, Gwathmey, Gutiérrez, Pagés, Dogliotti, Weese, Scharpff, Lundy.

44. Being anaesthetised to the point of respiratory arrest in tests related to artificial respiration; repeatedly exposed to prolonged anoxia in tests related to safe escape from doomed aircraft by parachute; and being thrown unconscious into deep water towards the evolvement of safe lifejackets! Gar Pask was also the most daunting of the examiners I faced in the orals for the Primary Fellowship in Anaesthesia.

course of action followed by others". In the larger scheme of things they are simply the individual links along the way, for that is how the pages of history are turned.[45]

Alongside the kaleidoscopic development of anaesthetic machines has come a parallel evolution in the actual means of producing and maintaining the state of anaesthesia, moving from the original use of a single inhalational anaesthetic to the battery of intravenous drugs now in vogue, with the regular introduction of new and supposedly better volatile agents. I remember the eager anticipation with which we greeted the arrival of halothane. This is mirrored by enthusiasm about the volatile agents in use today. They will pass into the sunset in the fullness of time, just like the old standby nitrous oxide. We seldom avoided its use, many of today's anaesthetists hardly use it at all. In its early descriptive designation as "laughing gas" nitrous oxide is perhaps the only name in our entire speciality which is universally recognised. Despite the fact that it has been given to countless millions of patients since it was first clinically promoted by Horace Wells in 1844, there was a recent suggestion that if its anaesthetic properties were only discovered today its disadvantages would have prevented its introduction into clinical practice.[46]

The cycles of repetition are almost limitless. Looking at letters in medical journals is a bit like playing Monopoly; the longer your game lasts the more those "go directly to jail" cards keep turning up! Medicine, surgery, anaesthesia… the speciality matters not a jot. Sir William Osler pointed out a century or so ago that the medical serpent has always had the propensity for jumping up and swallowing its own tail; recent correspondence about nitrous oxide re-emphasises that observation yet again. Somewhere in one of my cupboards lies an article by a very experienced Scottish anaesthetist whom I knew. The title, "To supplement or not?", illustrates a debate from the 1960s as to whether one needed to use a small percentage of halothane in addition to nitrous oxide in order to prevent awareness under anaesthesia. I contributed to the correspondence columns of that debate as a young registrar, for with the use of such a supplement not a part of the widely acclaimed Liverpool technique the occasional grey and sweating face of an anaesthetised patient caused many of us much concern. Four decades of progress – from agreement that something had to be added to nitrous oxide to prevent awareness to an expressed concern in 2002 that its abandonment might lead to an increased incidence of awareness![47] One's fascination lies not so much in the opinions, or with the new arguments thrown into the mix with the old, but rather in the fact that just as everything changes, nothing changes.

---

45. For more fascinating details on the pioneers of anaesthesia see J. Roger Maltby ed. *Notable Names in Anaesthesia*. London, Royal Society of Medicine Press, 2002.

46. Carter, J. A. and McAteer, P. *Anaesthesia* 2002; **57**, 1: 82.

47. Zorab, J. S. M. "Nitrous oxide." *Anaesthesia* 2002; **57**, 1: 82.

No less in medicine than any other field of human endeavour do we continue to rediscover – or think we have rediscovered – what we already know.

And as the many early pieces of apparatus, the heralded new agents and the innovative techniques which combined them – all introduced in their day as major advances – are replaced, the discarded equipment begins to gather dust in cupboards or be more happily displayed on museum shelves. The worldwide anaesthetic road which I have travelled has led from open drop ether and chloroform to a vastly changed era of highly sophisticated technology, with the introduction of the pulse oximeter to my mind perhaps the biggest single advance in my professional lifetime. If anyone of my vintage looks back at the methods they used in the past, they will be amused by what they did ten years ago, alarmed by what they did twenty years ago and astonished by what they did thirty years ago. To the generation which follows, old-fashioned methods appear outdated, archaic or dangerous and by modern standards perhaps even culpably negligent.

The major lesson from all of this, the major lesson of our own history, is that our efforts will be no different. Human knowledge may increase but human thinking stays the same. The same mistakes will be made and both the right and wrong conclusions reached – for both the right and the wrong reasons. As computerised techniques steadily increase, and as other yet unknown advances make their way into our armamentarium, the delivery of anaesthesia in the year 2050 will resemble 2010 as much as that year now resembles 1970.

Surgery, too, will change dramatically. Although no crystal ball is needed to recognise this fact, what it tells us about our current methods is largely unappreciated. The most common major surgical operation we encountered as newly qualified doctors in the early 1950s was partial gastrectomy for chronic peptic ulcer; at Hairmyres we used to assist with one or two such procedures a week. With the understanding and management of ulcer disease now totally transformed, an individual surgeon is now more likely to do only one or two similar cases per year, and for a different reason. Compare this with one of the most common major operations of recent times, coronary artery bypass surgery. With radical developments in this area absolutely certain in coming decades, how many of these procedures will be done by 2050? Stay around until then and you will find out!

Look still further if you are not convinced. The cycle which so often follows the appearance of a new drug is well recognised: enthusiastic introduction; increasing use succeeded by overuse and even misuse; recognition of significant side effects or other problems; denial followed by caution and then by limitation to specific conditions; eventual abandonment. Much less appreciated is the fact that the history of countless investigative or therapeutic procedures differs hardly at all, with many once vigorously advocated seen in hindsight to be questionable and more than a few even as frankly stupid.

External irradiation to the head, neck and upper thorax was once administered to treat a variety of conditions, including recurrent tonsillitis, acne, ringworm of the scalp and enlargement of the thymus gland. Although not appreciated at the time, the relatively small doses of radiation given during childhood increased the risk of subsequent development of both benign and malignant tumours of the thyroid gland. Radiation for tonsillitis, acne or ringworm?? We may look back askance at such advice today, or still further at the days of purging, blistering and cupping, but how often do we consider the possibility of counterparts in our own times?

As students at Glasgow's old Gartnavel Hospital in the early 1950s we witnessed the administration of unmodified electroshock therapy. It was not a pretty sight. Many strong arms were required to restrain the arching backs and flailing limbs as we passed in turn along the beds of large open wards, and if screens could hide the sights from the other patients they did nothing to protect them from the accompanying sounds. Over succeeding years we learned to administer these treatments in comparative privacy and to soften their side effects with intravenous hypnotics and muscle relaxants, yet long after it had been abandoned I remember assisting one psychiatrist who still insisted that the unmodified form of the treatment was necessary for selected patients. Such a practice would be condemned today almost as much as the gross misuse of the therapy in Montreal in the 1950s which had tacit encouragement and at least partial funding from the CIA.[48]

I was personally involved in a quite different example of misuse during my anaesthetic training, for together with our fellow registrars in psychiatry we were required to give short courses of ECT to patients with advanced metastatic cancer. A surgeon had noted that the history of many of his cancer cases indicated a correlation between the start of the condition and an extreme emotional upset, such as the death of a spouse. He speculated that the disease process might be halted, or even reversed, by ECT, and for a number of weeks we were part – a deeply unhappy part I may add – of a trial which succeeded only in increasing the physical and mental frailty of the unfortunate individuals involved.

By the mid-sixties Tom Baillie and I were giving anaesthetics in Dumfries for as many as a hundred ECTs in a week, this peak coming around the time of the introduction and general acceptance of the early anti-depressant drugs, and just a few years later a psychiatric colleague astonished me by enthusing over research about the use of a convulsant gas as an alternative to the electric current. I asked him

---

48. The Montreal psychiatrist at the centre of this scandal took his medical training in Glasgow alongside my uncle John Humble.

who would be expected to give this new agent. 'You fellows,' he replied. My look betrayed what I thought of that suggestion.

Will the day come when the application of an electric current to the brain will be looked back on only in curious terms? I do not know the answer to that question, but the fact that all of our methods will come under scrutiny and that many if not most of them will change is a message that must be passed on. While young physicians may view current practices as exciting and precise, the example of my cousin's illness (see "A difficult decision") dramatically emphasises the revolution which can take place in any branch of medicine. As the boundaries of our knowledge widen in every area, our new drugs and equipment, our operations, our treatment regimes and other techniques – all will become old, just as Belloste pointed out so simply close to three centuries ago. We must therefore question every single thing we do in the light of that knowledge and in the words of William Mushin, another of my examiners, 'train the doctors of tomorrow to be thinkers, not simply technicians'.

SOMETHING OF VALUE

If a man does away with his traditional way of living and throws away his good customs, he had better first make certain that he has something of value to replace them.
Basutu proverb

The philosophy of anaesthesia espoused by curare pioneer Stuart Cullen was an inspiration to many:

What is the safest and best anaesthetic in my hands for just this patient, for just this operation and for just this surgeon, and how can I make it most comfortable for the patient?[49]

With the ever-increasing use of day surgery the modern anaesthetist sees fewer and fewer patients personally before they arrive in the operating room. A straw poll of colleagues on both sides of the Atlantic garnered estimates from as high as seventy-five percent to as low as five percent and even one percent, these latter figures truly astonishing to those of us who derived much satisfaction from personal contact with patients. The latter will have been screened, certainly, at pre-assessment clinics and the like, and before major surgery been given the opportunity of talking with a member of the anaesthetic department. But if their eyes do not meet those of the attending anaesthetist until a few minutes prior to surgery, can Cullen's separate but interrelated questions still be fully addressed? The answer must surely lie in the relationships between all the parties concerned.

Surgeons come in many forms. I should know, for I have worked with them all. As their images pass before me today I see a quite remarkable gathering: tall and short; lean and fat; men (mostly) but quite a few women, one of the latter perhaps the most demanding individual I ever encountered; self-assured seniors and nervous juniors; down-to-earth individuals and pedantic ones; fast operators and not so fast

---

49. Gordh, T. "How anaesthesiology came to Sweden." *Acta Anaesthesiol Scand* 1998; **42:** *Supplementum 113*, 37.

operators; early risers and persistent latecomers; easy-going mortals and workaholics; some prone to anger, including instrument and tantrum throwers, and others composed under all circumstances; those with a good bedside manner and some who lacked that very quality; a few who tackled procedures they had little experience in and some who continued to operate when they should have taken retirement; excellent and poor communicators; co-operative colleagues and the occasional temporary foe; dedicated teachers and some who paid scant attention to junior medical and nursing staff; and above all many wonderful clinicians and friends. Let me give a few examples of their differing character traits, remembering some affectionately by name.

One of the surgeons we worked for during our pre-registration year was dapper in the extreme and never lost for words. The telephone in the doctors' lounge rang at eleven pm: 'Mr Smith has just woken up from his anaesthetic. He wants to know why the dressing for his hernia operation is on the left side instead of the right.'

Remembering how slowly things had gone earlier that day, with the surgeon vainly trying to identify a hernial sac but succeeding only in finding a small lipoma of the spermatic cord, we rang him at home.

'Oh… I see… thanks for letting me know… better give him a shot of morphine. I'll be in first thing in the morning.'

The conversation the following morning went as follows:

'Well, Mr Smith, you'll be wondering why your bandage is on the left instead of the right. Well… you see, when we got you relaxed enough under the anaesthetic, we discovered a defect on both sides[50] and decided to operate on the left side first. Just as well, too, just as well, for we discovered a small tumour there which we were able to remove totally. It will give you no further problem of any kind. We'll do the other side next week. You'll be as good as new again.'

One of the most grateful patients I can ever remember left hospital two weeks later. He bore twin scars and imagined himself rescued from cancer. In actual fact the admitting clerk had typed "left" instead of "right" on the operating list and the admitting house surgeon had been on his afternoon off. None of the rest of us had examined the patient. Indefensible? By today's standards certainly, but those were simpler times when trust had not been threatened and indeed was still of mutual benefit.

Bertie England had a build to rival "Pop" Burton, even St Nicholas. He delivered our first daughter at Forest Gate in the north-east of London, a busy unit which he ran more or less on his own. But while Bertie could certainly look after mothers and babies, he never seemed to be able to tie his operating pants securely, and for them

---

50. This comment can best be described as a terminological inexactitude. The tumour was a simple lipoma.

to fall to the floor during a Caesarean section was a common and eagerly anticipated occurrence. With the task of restoration usually given to a junior circulating nurse, who had to grope blindly inside his operating gown, the subsequent hilarity in the female changing room is not hard to imagine!

Mr —, a surgeon I was working with in the south of England, had little time for any junior nurse with whom he was required to work. Finishing a gastrectomy one day he was informed by a young trainee that the instrument count showed one towel clip to be missing. Two of her senior colleagues confirmed the count.

'Do it again… count everything. Dammit, it must be under the drapes!'

'Sorry, sir…' (a few moments later) '…we're still one towel clip short.'

Continuing to insist that the offending object must be out of sight somewhere on the floor, or that the initial instrument count had been incorrect, Mr — rapidly completed the peritoneal closure. He then left the remainder of the operation to his assistant and went off to change. An x-ray technician was sent for, a plain film quickly confirming that the missing instrument was still inside the abdomen. No apologies of any kind were given, merely abrupt instructions to the surgical registrar to re-open the wound. By then Mr — was half-way to the front door of the hospital, already late for the first of his afternoon's private patients.

The late Fred Conroy, a Canadian of Irish extraction, used to appear in the doctors' lounge on St Patrick's Day wearing an emerald green suit and tie, with shoes to match. He did no operating that day, but dispensed Irish coffee freely. He remains the only surgeon with whom I have ever started a whole day's operating list on the best of terms, had a fierce argument with in the middle of the morning, spent the next two hours working together without uttering a single word and finished up at four in the afternoon again the best of friends.

A fine story is told of Fred from the days before I met him, when the Sisters of the Grey Nuns of Montreal were still the major force in the running of the Edmonton General Hospital. Losing his temper in the operating room, he called one of the nuns 'a son of a —'. As he stepped through the front door of the hospital at seven am the following morning there was a loud message over the intercom: 'Dr Conroy to Sister Superior's office immediately.' Fred gathered his thoughts, preparing his version of the events of the previous day. He never got the chance to open his mouth.

'Dr Conroy… you called one of my Sisters "a son of a —" yesterday. Let me make one thing quite clear. One of my Sisters may act like "a son of a —", but under no possible circumstances are you ever to call any of them "a son of a —"! Is that quite clear? Good morning, Dr Conroy.'

The interview had ended, with Fred lost for words for about the only time in his life!

A surgeon's speed may be less important than imagined. To urge a comparatively slow and meticulous operator to suddenly become a rapid one may be no better than to urge a rapid one to slow down. Much better for them to work at the pace with which they are most comfortable – often a reflection of their character. There were some acute emergencies, however, when I rejoiced to find a particular individual on call – as well as one or two occasions when my heart sank. Fastest of all in my experience was obstetrician Angus Boyd. If a baby ever got into serious trouble inside the womb, no surgeon on earth could have got it out of the abdomen quicker than Angus.

Individual surgeons often excel in a specific area. This is not to say they operate less well at other sites, but simply that if I required either gall bladder or thyroid surgery my choice of surgeon might well be different. If you arrive in a new city and don't know which surgeon may be best in a particular field, ask an anaesthetist, for that individual sees more from the head of the table than he or she is ever given credit for. The view may not always be an ideal one. I have watched a young surgical trainee in Britain get totally lost in a difficult hernia repair, entering the bladder in error, and seen an elderly surgeon in Canada equally lost during a thyroidectomy, inadvertently entering the oesophagus and necessitating several days of intensive care for the patient; this disaster happened several months after our Department of Anaesthesia had advised the chief of surgery of concerns about this individual's continuing ability for any major surgery. I've also been in many different operating rooms where a part-time surgeon has encountered enormous trouble during the removal of an acute appendix, at once the simplest and the most difficult of all emergency operations.

Some surgeons I worked with appeared to be lucky in addition to being good, their patients experiencing fewer complications than colleagues with comparable practices. Alan Mowat was a prime example. The brother of George Mowat, the long-time chief of the surgical unit one floor above that of Pop Burton at the Glasgow Royal, Alan spent almost his entire surgical career in the Colonial Medical Service. In semi-retirement by the time I met him in Kenya, he still relished the challenge of a difficult abdominal case. Despite certain unusual aspects of technique, every patient I referred to him used to do extraordinarily well. From the head of the table it was often fun to watch. Whenever he got into any difficulty, with exposure of a gall bladder in a very obese patient for example, he would rip off his surgical gloves, roll up his sleeves and get down to business in earnest. Any remonstrations regarding this habit were quietly ignored, as were attempts on the part of the circulating nurse to wipe his brow. Alan used to sweat profusely in the operating room. As the drips fell directly into the open abdomen, he would gesture the offender away, his

Scots accent even more evident than usual: 'Nurse... have you never heard of the antibiotic properties of sweat?'

Yet while the patients of the other surgeons in the town might develop an infected wound, Alan's never did. Technically correct in his assertion regarding the natural composition of human sweat, he remains the only surgeon in my experience who made any attempt to turn this fact to his advantage!!

Are these stories and comments about a few of my surgical colleagues, chosen from countless incidents over a period of four decades, of any real relevance? Certainly they are, for they help to show how well the anaesthetist can come to know and indeed needs to know the temperament of the surgeon[51] and to illustrate the relevance of their working relationship. Neurosurgeon Harvey Cushing realised many, many years ago that his operative results were much better when he worked with the same anaesthetist and the same operating team, very significantly poorer with continual changes in those personnel. The politicians, bureaucrats and hospital administrators of our modern world would do well to review Cushing's writings, for they have little understanding of the full significance of this operative partnership. Never having worked in an operating room, they imagine that the end result will be the same provided a surgeon, an anaesthetist, a patient and the appropriate nursing staff can be scheduled to be in the same place at the same time.

When economics and political expediency led to hospital downsizing in the city of Edmonton a number of years ago it was decided to merge the coverage of some types of anaesthesia at the four major hospitals. Rather than working only at one site, individual anaesthetists were required to rotate between the four institutions at regular and fairly short intervals. A splendid idea to those who dreamt it up, but in reality something of an accident waiting to happen. Surgeons were greeted by strangers, some of whom then found themselves involved in complicated surgical procedures with which they were not totally familiar, or else in surroundings where drugs and other ancillary equipment were stored in unfamiliar places. No one was happy. Problems arose, predictably, and not all of them minor, with patients suffering as a result. There are many intangibles which influence different aspects of the entire surgical process. Significant complications can stem from lack of co-operation or understanding between surgeon and anaesthetist and a post-operative death in a hospital I worked in many years ago was directly attributable to such a situation. Familiarity between members of a regularly functioning operative team is a time-honoured practice which remains a good custom. While the above city-wide rotations were abandoned some time later, in this era of increasingly impersonal health care the decision makers would do well to look before they leap. Patients can be the losers. The tradition of the Basutu people tells us why.

---

51. The reverse equally applies.

So much for surgeons; how do anaesthetists differ? Although as varied as any professional group, when compared to the surgical ranks they include far fewer "type A" personalities and are seldom overweight, a combination which probably says something about our lifestyles. I do not think my colleague Ron Gregg will object to my saying that he might be an exception in the first of these categories. He proved the ideal person to deal with one particularly aggressive patient. It was a Tuesday morning. A high-powered nursing administrator from a different province had been admitted following an unexpected early miscarriage. After answering his routine questions regarding the state of her health, she demanded to know if he was good at his job. Ron was never lost for words. 'On Mondays, Wednesdays and Fridays only!' he shot back, a very subdued individual being wheeled into the operating room several minutes later. I'm not quite sure how I might have dealt with that particular question. Whatever their personality, however, anaesthetists must respond to differing and difficult situations while only rarely giving outward evidence of inner feelings. When I think of some valued colleagues who have died at a relatively early age, I think back to the words of one surgeon. This is what he wrote for his friend's obituary:

> *That appearance of calm so essential to the surgeon in the face of impending disaster and exhibited by every competent anaesthetist in times of crisis exacts a price which to my knowledge has never been adequately defined or assessed.*

Ask any of your friends how they have reacted to anaesthesia. The response will almost always relate to the subject of post-operative nausea or vomiting. Enquire further and they will tell you of the ease of induction by means of an intravenous drug. Of what happens in between they will know little and understand less. The hands of surgeons are directly guided by what their eyes see. The challenge of anaesthesia lies in coping with a wide range of physiological, pharmacological and surgical responses, the specific causes of which may often be hidden. The human body is a marvellous machine, but it is not a perfect one. Nor is it a perfect world. Things can go wrong, and do go wrong. Significant life-threatening situations can happen during short procedures as well as during prolonged ones, whilst all manner of relatively minor complications occur, some days to almost every patient, some days to none. All must be managed correctly, the aim of each anaesthetist being to develop a system which in their hands keeps such complications to an unavoidable minimum. Gone are the single agent days of ether and chloroform. As a modern anaesthetic can now involve the administration of as many as twenty or more drugs by a variety of different routes, the practice of anaesthesia conceals far more variation and interest than even many physicians suspect.

Although it would have taken a major textbook to cover every difficulty, a final few may be briefly mentioned. Just as in the flying of an aircraft, problems can occur during both the induction and the immediate recovery periods. Control of the airway is paramount, as has already been noted, but never more so than during neurosurgical procedures or operations performed with the patient in less than usual positions.[52] Respiratory difficulties are commonplace, particularly when dealing with the lungs of smokers; fluid and electrolyte shifts occur regularly, sometimes to extremes, as evidenced by a patient of mine who absorbed excessive amounts of the fluid used to irrigate his bladder during a transurethral prostatectomy under spinal anaesthesia, becoming temporarily blind as a result;[53] and cardiac arrhythmias and swings in blood pressure are part and parcel of the whole response to surgery and anaesthesia. Our job is to monitor those changes, adjust to them, and prevent their deterioration with as little fuss as possible, advising the surgeon as and when we think it appropriate. We must also remain ready to recognise and respond to a variety of allergic reactions, the most acute and dangerous of which any individual anaesthetist may only see once or twice in a professional lifetime.

'Anaesthesia is ninety-five percent boredom and five percent sheer panic.' I have often heard that type of comment made. As I have explained to many students, I consider it nonsense. The anaesthetist who allows boredom to edge into his or her daily routine is forgetting what the speciality is all about, our whole raison d'être in fact, for this could lead to the missing of a minor alteration or trend in any of the physiological parameters which must be followed, and to being less well prepared to take the necessary corrective action. How much better is this description:

> *Each administration of an anaesthetic drug is unique, and even*
> *where the same drug is used, no two cases are exactly alike. For*
> *the true anaesthesiologist, the management of an anaesthetic is a*
> *continued and fascinating study, a never failing source of applied*
> *physiology and pharmacology in the human being.*[54]

The doyen of Swedish anaesthesia, Torsten Gordh, wrote the above words in 1944. One of the delighted discoveries of my early career was of the indwelling needle he devised. Today's juniors might be astonished to learn just how much the Gordh

---

52. Certain procedures require the patient to be in a sitting, prone or knee-chest position.

53. Treatment of the electrolyte imbalance restored his sight within two hours.

54. Gordh, T. "How anaesthesiology came to Sweden." *Acta Anaesthesiol Scand* 1998; **42:** *Supplementum 113*, 37.

needle, or the alternative Mitchell needle, was relied upon by the anaesthetists of the 1950s, an era when intravenous infusions during routine surgery were comparatively rare. It was my great privilege to hear Gordh speak at the World Congress of Anesthesiology in Hamburg in 1980. His didactic statement is as true today as on the day when he set it down. When he went to sit at the feet of Ralph Waters in Madison, Wisconsin in 1938, Gordh was taught that the anaesthetist should see, hear or feel every breath taken by every patient. There is still validity in that advice, for it urges the anaesthetist – despite all the technology of the modern operating room – to stay as close as is possible to the patient and take absolutely nothing for granted. That old Greek motto was wisely chosen – *we watch closely those who sleep.*

Cullen's maxim spoke of surgeon, anaesthetist and patient. Before I talk a bit more about our relationship with patients there is another partnership to acknowledge which has even greater value than the one we have with our surgical colleagues, a relationship without which the job of any anaesthetist would be impossible. I'm referring, of course, to our association with the nursing staff of operating and recovery rooms and the trained personnel who work alongside them.

There were no technicians in the hospitals where I gave my first anaesthetics, only nursing staff and porters. The latter did a great deal more than fetch and carry patients. I've worked in Africa with the help of a few who could speak no English and from many others I remember with gratitude Tom, John and Bobby at the Dumfries and Galloway Royal Infirmary. John once saved the life of a hypoxic child by responding immediately and correctly to my urgent request for an endotracheal tube of a specific size and shape from one of many in different drawers and cabinets of the adjoining room, while Tom used his capable hands and common sense to do maintenance work on our anaesthetic equipment.

To learn that an untrained porter had been given our blessing to act in such a capacity would be anathema to a major equipment company today, yet around that same time one of the British Oxygen Company's own service technicians only escaped being the cause of a dreadful tragedy through the quick thinking of one of my predecessors as registrar at the Kingston Hospital.[55] Beginning a brief anaesthetic in the labour ward one morning, he ventilated the patient with one hundred percent oxygen, becoming alarmed to see her colour go from pink to blue. Alarm turned to dismay when further oxygen changed the blue to almost black. Knowing that this particular anaesthetic machine was not in regular daily use, he quickly asked if anyone else had touched it in recent days. 'The serviceman from British Oxygen was here the day before yesterday,' came the reply.

There was only one possible remedy. Strange as it might seem today, a Boyle's machine of that particular vintage was equipped with bypass levers for both oxygen

---

55. Kalra, A. and Doughty, A. G. "The Wrong Gas." *Anaesthesia* 1963; **18**, 2: 234-236.

and nitrous oxide and a few breaths of what was supposed to be the latter saw the patient's colour begin to improve, then rapidly return to a reassuring pink. The explanation? At the end of a routine service call a fully qualified individual had managed to transpose the lines of supply from the oxygen and nitrous oxide cylinders, a manoeuvre made impossible in later models through the implementation of a number of fail-safe measures.

Graduates of technical schools began to play an increasing role in operating theatres on a day-to-day basis as the art of anaesthesia turned into a science. Some were qualified in bio-mechanics, others in respiratory care or came from hospital labs and x-ray departments. As surgery advanced into the era of transplantation technicians with even more specialised skills were needed. Robots will mean more again, and the work of major hospitals today would be impossible without this kind of expertise.

Yet the real sheet anchors of my career came in the persons of the nursing staff. Operating room nurses are a special breed and not every entrant into their ranks has the ability, temperament or desire to join them, a fact which seems to have escaped the minds of the modern nursing hierarchy. In the past every junior nurse was required to take three months of training. A "natural" was almost immediately recognised and their vocation steadily encouraged. By the time of my retirement, however, we had come to the astonishing situation in Edmonton in which the only practical experience of the operating area which young university-based nurses received before graduation came through following one patient through one operation during a single day. Perhaps some sanity has returned since then, or will do so in the future. If it does not, something else of the greatest value will have been lost.

It would be invidious for me to mention by name any of the hundreds of nurses with whom I have had the pleasure of working. No further stories need be recounted for in every one already described one or more of their number has played a vital role. All were made bearable with the good humour, patience and skill of so many well-remembered faces. Every patient undergoing surgery owes them a tremendous debt. I can only give them my thanks.

ALL IN THE DAY'S WORK

For us an operation is an incident in the day's work, but
for our patients it may be the sternest and most dreaded of
all trials, for the mysteries of life and death surround it,
and it must be faced alone.
Baron Moynihan of Leeds (1865-1936)

Together with a small group of other anaesthetists I spent a marvellous Saturday morning at St Margaret's Hospital, Epping in 1963, watching the late Donald Bateman give the smoothest possible demonstration of the now forgotten technique of blind nasal intubation under ether. Earlier that same year he had expressed his own particular philosophy of anaesthesia.[56] One phrase he used in that article has lost nothing of its meaning with the passage of time:

We cannot remind ourselves too often that every time we induce
anaesthesia we are inducing a process which, if it escapes control,
will assuredly end the patient's life.

The events of a September morning in the south-west of England just three years later underlined the prophetic wisdom behind that counsel. Two completely healthy patients undergoing routine surgery inhaled nitrous oxide from a cylinder which was later found to be contaminated with the higher oxides of nitrogen. The first patient died; the second was saved by presence of mind and action in the face of a totally unexpected situation.[57] One other similar and fatal case occurred elsewhere in the same region. During the full investigation of the catastrophe it transpired that one of the several vital purity tests routinely carried out during the manufacture of nitrous oxide had been omitted or misread by a sick technician who should not have reported for work. While this type of occurrence is quite exceptional, it illustrates how a total

---

56. Bateman, D. A. "Philosophy of Anaesthesia." *Anaesthesia* 1963; **18**, 2: 185-188.

57. "Higher oxides of nitrogen as an impurity in nitrous oxide." *British Journal of Anaesthesia* 1967; **39**, 5: 343-344 (whole issue devoted to this and related topics).

disaster can happen in anaesthesia without any fault on the part of the anaesthetist and although some may worry about the bluntness of Donald Bateman's warning it has to be put into the context of the numbers who pass safely through the operating rooms of the world.

Donald's personal approach to his work did not meet with the universal approval of his colleagues, in particular his contention that the relationship between surgeon and anaesthetist should be comparable to that which exists between a commanding officer and his adjutant:[58]

> *The situation existing between the surgeon and anaesthetist is of vital importance in determining the quality of the surgery performed... It follows that there is no place ever for a temperamental anaesthetist. He (or she) must be the one sound, tranquillising and stabilising influence in the operating room... orderly in mind, equable in temperament, slow to anger and something of a diplomat. He should not seek the limelight for it will seldom fall upon him. An accompanist rather than an artiste, his satisfaction (which must always remain private) is in his knowledge that without him the surgical performance would not have been possible.*

While I have little argument with the sentiments expressed in the first half of that paragraph, I believe that the image of our speciality has suffered from our very failure to seek the limelight. The result of this failure is only too obvious. A quite recent issue of a Canadian current affairs magazine included a four-page survey of the marvels of modern surgery. The only reference to anaesthesia was the single use of the word "anesthetized" in reference to a patient lying on an operating table, while surgeons were described as "the traditional crown princes of the medical establishment, the healers with hands of silk... soon to be forced to share the glory with the computer crowd". I yield to no one in my admiration of our surgical colleagues, nor of the technical wizards in other disciplines, but such language is utter nonsense. Modern medicine is a team game, with neither crown princes nor commoners as players. I was amused recently to read extended details of surgery and surgeons in regard to a difficult operation on a well-known Irish-trained racehorse.[59] 'Danoli made an excellent recovery from the anaesthetic,' reported the surgeon, with no mention at all of the anaesthetists. It seems as though our anonymity extends to other fields!

---

58. Cricket commentator Peter West compared the partnership which develops between the great bowlers and wicketkeepers of cricket to that which exists between surgeon and anaesthetist, a much better analogy.

59. Foley, T. and Taub, M. *Danoli – The People's Champion.* London, Robson Books, 1997.

When members of the public turn to possible sources of information on anaes-thesia, what do they find? On their television screens they see the emergency depart-ment portrayed as the centre of the modern hospital, with precious little reference to the role of the anaesthetist; in classic movies from the past they may be shown that person hiding behind a copy of *The Times*; and in novels relating to anaesthesia they will be presented with highly improbable or futuristic plots. Even the medical literature may not be much better. In listing his forty most important advances of the twentieth century, a widely read editorialist failed to make any mention of the breakthrough with curare, the connection which opened the door to the modern era of surgery. Since patients today cannot possibly imagine undergoing surgery in the presence of constant and excruciating pain, no public memory remains of days when this was an unavoidable consequence of life, no memory either of days when the concept of pain relief in childbirth was just a mirage, nor of the fact that it was the advent of anaesthesia in the mid-1800s that helped these times to change. Only rarely today do the general population give any thought to the successors of Long, Wells, Morton and Simpson, who in the United Kingdom now form the largest single group of hospital-based specialist physicians. Significant numbers of them work in less familiar areas, both in and beyond hospital walls, where different challenges are faced from a wide variety of groups: expectant mothers in obstetric units requir-ing epidural analgesia; the sickest of individuals in intensive care units where an anaesthetist is often in overall charge; patients of all ages who require relief of acute post-operative pain; longer term problems in clinics for the relief of chronic pain; and the critically ill who need the care of trauma and major disaster teams. The anaesthetist of today is a major player in all of these vitally important areas.

In their more traditional place as partners to their surgical colleagues, and with hospital care becoming increasingly more impersonal in the larger centres, fewer and fewer may be able to meet individual patients ahead of the morning of surgery. Can we blame those same patients for not remembering our names if the voice which greets them is that of a stranger, especially if they understand little of what we do and almost nothing of the problems we face? I indicated in my introduction to these reflections that I do not believe that the image of anaesthesia can be improved by largely impersonal means, or by the changing of a name or a professional society's motto, still less by talking to politicians. It will only improve if anaesthetists can find fresh and innovative ways of bringing the full scope of their work to the attention of their patients. There were more opportunities in the past for personal contact and I have long since lost count of the numbers who expressed appreciation for time spent with them the night before their anaesthesia or for continuing to visit them post-operatively, occasions I may add in which all manner of things used to come up for discussion – even questions about their operations which they had been afraid to ask the surgeon. Although such a routine may be much less practical today, every stretcher approaching the operating area still carries an individual in a vulnerable state of mind as Lord Moynihan so clearly pointed out a very long time ago, and much of that vulnerability relates to the loss of control and uncertainty associated with anaesthesia.

I believe that as those individuals present themselves for surgery they will do so more easily if they know more about anaesthesia, about anaesthetics and about the men and women who are about to look after them. How this can best be achieved is for a different generation to decide. It should be a two-way street. Patients must learn to ask more, though they may need encouragement to do so; anaesthetists must be prepared to blow their own trumpets more, especially on a one-to-one basis, and to find their own individual ways of interpreting Cullen's old maxim.

'That's a fairly responsible job,' my opponent on the golf course said all those years ago. Of course it is – the practice of anaesthesia is a very responsible job. I hope that these brief recollections may have opened a few eyes to the term Richard Gordon chose as the title of his novel of the birth of anaesthesia. *The Sleep of Life*[60] is a book which many lay individuals would enjoy. It should be made compulsory reading for every trainee in anaesthesia.

---

60. Gordon, R. *The Sleep of Life*. London, Heinemann, 1975.

ENVOI

Thinking back more than sixty years now to the beginning of my university studies I feel sure that my decision to enter medicine was in large measure due to my uncle, John Humble. With a practice close to the River Thames and Hampton Court Palace in the distant south of England, not to mention the few hundred yards which separated his home from the seven-furlong start on Hurst Park Racecourse, it somehow seemed like the end of the rainbow. Although I never worked with him, a good friend from the year behind us at Glasgow did, and he still lives happily in East Molesey. My footsteps led me elsewhere and I cannot blame "The Doctor" for my eventual entry into anaesthesia, that choice coming through a curious mixture of travel, family circumstances and winds of change. I hope that he would approve of the well-known quotation I am choosing to end with. The words are those of an individual he knew well, one of the great figures in British medicine from the century just ended, whose textbook *Clinical Methods* served as a bible for countless numbers of students. They sum up the concerns which John and I shared over many years, concerns in which other contemporaries now join about the future of the doctor-patient relationship and about a medical profession which we see in many areas as having crossed its own Rubicon. I have taken the liberty of adding the word "always" to the quotation. In the light of the astonishing advances since his times I do not think that the man known to his students as "Bobby Hutch" would object.

I think there should be a new petition in the litany to be read in hospital chapels or wherever doctors and nurses do, or ought to, congregate. It might be as follows: from inability to let well alone; from too much zeal for the new and contempt for what is old; from putting knowledge before wisdom, science always before art and cleverness before common sense; from treating patients as cases and from making the cure of the disease more grievous than the endurance of the same, Good Lord, deliver us.

Sir Robert Hutchison (1871-1960)